Ready-to-

LANGUAGE
ARTICULATION&
DEVELOPMENT
ACTIVITIES
for Special Children

Anita R. McMillan

Illustrated by
Eileen Gerne Ciavarella

**THE CENTER FOR APPLIED
RESEARCH IN EDUCATION**
West Nyack, New York 10995

Library of Congress Cataloging-in-Publication Data

McMillan, Anita Reeves
   Ready-to-use language articulation and development activities for
special children / Anita Reeves McMillan; illustrated by Eileen Gerne
Ciavarella.
     p.   cm.
  ISBN 0-87628-807-7
  1. Speech therapy for children. 2. Creative activities and seat
work. I. Title.
RJ496.S7M393 1992
618.92'85506—dc20
                                                        91-29872
                                                         CIP

**The Center for Applied
Research in Education**
Business Information & Publishing Division
West Nyack, NY 10995
Simon & Schuster, A Paramount Communications Company

Printed in the United States of America

ABOUT THE AUTHOR

Anita Reeves McMillan is currently a speech pathologist for the Marion School District #2 in Mullins, SC. She has worked with students who have multiple speech and language handicaps, mentally retarded students, learning disabled students and students with English as a second language. These students range from the ages of 4 to 21.

She received her degree in speech pathology from Western Kentucky University in Bowling Green, KY and has a degree in music from Volunteer State College in Gallatin, TN.

She is past president of the Marion-Dillon Speech Association for School Speech Pathologists and has served on the committee for Speech-Language Pathologists in the Public Schools for the South Carolina Speech, Hearing and Language Association. She is presently helping to form a support group for learning disabled children.

ABOUT THE BOOK

The purpose of *Ready-to-Use Language Articulation and Development Activities for Special Children* is to give speech and/or language disordered children the opportunity to have "fun" with words, thus enhancing articulation skills, language development and reading skills. The book also gives students practice at following directions, helps to expand students' vocabulary, and can help improve expressive language and comprehension of language.

The book includes activities with the following phonemes, (ch, d, f, g, j, k, l, r, s, sh, t, v). Each phoneme has six activities: word circles, scrambled words, dotted words, crossword puzzles, word finds, and secret codes. Each of these activities provides the student with practice with their target sound in the initial, medial, and final position of words. Having the same activities for each phoneme enables the therapist to have a complete articulation/language workbook for all students in one complete volume. This enables the speech pathologist to use the same activity per session for groups which will save valuable preparation time and save time during the therapy session because the therapist will only have to give one set of directions to the entire group. The therapist can then devote more time to the individual students on correct production of the disordered phoneme and/or language and vocabulary development.

The worksheets in the book provide a wide range of vocabulary words which make good conversation starters. They are also versatile in that the students can work on these worksheets during therapy, or they can be used as homework or classwork, thus promoting carryover.

This book has special features: a section entitled "Additional Activities to Use with the Worksheets" and a complete answer key for each worksheet.

The book can be used by anyone working with children of varying articulation and language needs and ability levels, such as Speech-Language Pathologists, special education teachers, and regular classroom teachers.

Anita Reeves McMillan

ADDITIONAL ACTIVITIES
TO USE WITH THE WORKSHEETS

For Articulation

1. Have each student roll a die and say a word from the worksheet the number of times shown on the die.
2. Have the students make up their own puzzle using words they can already say correctly.
3. Have the students use the words from the worksheets in a carrier phrase, such as "I see the _____" or "I have a _____."
4. Play "I'm going on a trip and taking _____" (use a word from the worksheet).
5. Have the students sing a song that uses some of the words from the worksheets.
6. Have the students say a nursery rhyme that uses some of the words from the worksheet.
7. Have the students think of more words with a given sound.
8. Have the students draw a large flower stem. Have them draw a petal on the flower each time they say one of the worksheet words correctly.
9. Have the students build a block tower (one block per word) each time they say a word correctly.
10. Write the words from the worksheet on individual cards. Give the student the card if he or she can say the word on the card correctly. Use the carrier phrase: "Give me the _____."
11. Ask the students to say the words from the worksheet into a tape recorder or language master.
12. Read a familiar fairy tale or story, leaving out certain words. Let the students say one of the words from the worksheet in place of the omitted word to make up a funny story.
13. Have the students think of words that rhyme with the words on the worksheet.
14. Ask the students to raise their hand when they hear a word from the worksheet while you read a story.
15. Have the students draw and cut out pictures of the words from the worksheet. Then tell a flannel board story using the cutouts. Whenever you place a student's cutout on the flannel board, the student must say the word.
16. Have the children say as many words from the worksheet as they can in one sentence.
17. Put a large picture of a clown with no nose on the wall or chalkboard. Have the students cut out round pieces of paper. If a student says a word from his or her worksheet correctly, the student may then give the clown a nose.
18. As each student correctly says a word from the worksheet, have him or her write it on a poster for all to see.
19. Draw a tic-tac-toe board on the chalkboard. Have the students say the words from the worksheet and then write them on the board and play tic-tac-toe.
20. Have the students play charades using the words from the worksheets.
21. Have the children use modeling clay to make the shape of the words from the worksheet.

For language development

1. Use the worksheets to teach categorization skills. Have the students put the words from the worksheet into categories, such as animal, person, food, furniture, tool, place, game, clothes, etc.
2. Start a story and have the students add to the story using words from the worksheet.
3. Ask the students *who, what, where,* and *when* questions about the words from the worksheets.
4. Have each student draw pictures of each word from the worksheet and place them in a bag. Pick a picture from the bag and hold it up for the student to see. The student must describe or tell as much as possible about the picture. If the student is unable to do this, the picture goes back into the bag to be taught later.

5. Describe one of the words from the worksheet to each student. If the student guesses the word, he or she is given points. If the student cannot guess the word, put it aside to be taught later.
6. Use the words from the worksheets to teach antonyms, synonyms, definitions, grammar, verb tense, compound words, root words, prefixes, suffixes, syllibication, letter-sound association, plurals, silent letters, contractions, alphabetizing, long and short vowels, etc. For example, have the students
    a. Circle the words on the worksheet that are nouns.
    b. Color a word blue if it is a verb.
    c. Put a square next to a word if it has a silent letter.
    d. Color all of the compound words purple.
    e. Color a word green if it has three syllables.
    f. Make plurals of the singular nouns on the worksheet.
    g. Make contractions of some of the words.
    h. Color all prefixes and suffixes yellow.
    i. Underline the consonants in each word on the worksheet and then say the word, being sure to make all of the sounds in each word.
    j. Divide the words into syllables and then say the words, being sure to say all of the syllables.

For Word Circles and Dotted Words: to enhance articulation

1. Have the students draw pictures of the words on the back of the worksheet.
2. Ask the student to color in the letters used to spell the word with his or her sound
3. Let each student draw two sets of pictures for each word on the back of an index card. The student shuffles the cards and places them face down. The student turns two cards over and names the pictures. If the cards match, the student puts them aside. The activity continues until all cards have been matched.
4. Have the students draw or write the words from the worksheet on a long strip of paper. Hold up a large picture of an object (monster, animal, etc.) with an open, cutout mouth. Have the students take turns feeding their paper strips to the object by saying, "My monster ate a _____."
5. Let each student cut out the word circles after coloring in the correct letters and place them face down. The student then mixes up the circles and tries to guess which circle has a certain word with his or her sound. If the student guesses correctly, he or she turns the circle face up. The student continues to play until all circles are face up.
6. Make a paper plate spinner by giving each student a paper plate, brad fastener, and paper spinner. The students are to draw a face in the center of the plate and write the words from the worksheet around the edge of the plate. Attach the spinner. Let each student spin the spinner and say the word that the spinner points to. The student is awarded five points if he or she says the word correctly.
7. Have the students cut out their circles and draw a picture of the word on the back of the circle. Place the circles in a bag. Each student reaches into the bag with eyes closed to get a circle. The student looks at the circle and says the word. If the student says the word correctly, he or she keeps the circle. The circles that are not pronounced correctly go back into the bag for further practice.

For Secret Codes, Scrambled Words, Word Finds, and Crossword Puzzles: to enhance articulation.

1. Have each student number the words in the Word Box, with no two students having the same number. Then call out a number at random. The student with that number must say the word correctly. If the student does so, he or she covers the word with a small strip of paper. The winner is the first one to cover all the words in his or her Word Box.

2. Have the students write words from the worksheet all over a piece of paper. Each student then drops a paper clip or other small object onto the paper and says the word on which it lands.
3. Have a beanbag toss. The students must say a word from the worksheet and toss a beanbag to another student, who in turn says one of the words from the worksheet and tosses the bag to another student.
4. Design a barrier game. Write words from the worksheet in each space of the game, and give each student a copy of the game. The students must say the words correctly in each space before proceeding to the next space.

ACKNOWLEDGMENTS

I would like to acknowledge the speech students who have provided me with new and helpful insights into communication disorders, and my family for never providing a dull moment.

CONTENTS

Scrambled Words (Initial, Medial, Final Positions)

Word Find (Initial, Medial, Final Positions)

Crossword Puzzle (Initial, Medial, Final Positions)

ACTIVITIES FOR /J/ • 81

Word Circles (Initial, Medial, Final Positions)

Dotted Words (Initial, Medial, Final Positions)

Secret Codes (Initial, Medial, Final Positions)

Scrambled Words (Initial, Medial, Final Positions)

Word Find (Initial, Medial, Final Positions)

Crossword Puzzle (Initial, Medial, Final Positions)

ACTIVITIES FOR /K/ • 101

Word Circles (Initial, Medial, Final Positions)

Dotted Words (Initial, Medial, Final Positions)

Secret Codes (Initial, Medial, Final Positions)

Scrambled Words (Initial, Medial, Final Positions)

Word Find (Initial, Medial, Final Positions)

Crossword Puzzle (Initial, Medial, Final Positions)

ACTIVITIES FOR /L/ • 121

Word Circles (Initial, Medial, Final Positions)

Dotted Words (Initial, Medial, Final Positions)

Secret Codes (Initial, Medial, Final Positions)

Scrambled Words (Initial, Medial, Final Positions)

Word Find (Initial, Medial, Final Positions)

Crossword Puzzle (Initial, Medial, Final Positions)

ACTIVITIES FOR /R/ • 141

Word Circles (Initial, Medial, Final Positions)

Dotted Words (Initial, Medial, Final Positions)

Secret Codes (Initial, Medial, Final Positions)

Scrambled Words (Initial, Medial, Final Positions)

Word Find (Initial, Medial, Final Positions)

Crossword Puzzle (Initial, Medial, Final Positions)

ACTIVITIES FOR /CH/

Name _____   Date _____

WORD CIRCLES

/CH/ INITIAL POSITION

FIND EVERY THIRD LETTER to find out what the puzzle says. Start at the arrow.

_____ Say each word _____ times.
_____ Learn the definition of each word.
_____ Write a sentence for each word.
_____ Make up a story using some of the words from the puzzle.
_____ Draw pictures of some of the words from the puzzle.
_____ Play "I Spy." Look around the classroom and find the words or the objects they represent.

_____ .

Answer: _____

Answer: _____

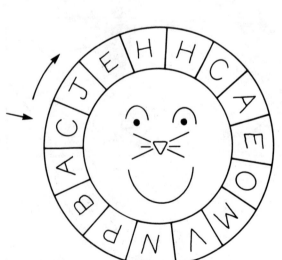

Answer: _____

Answer: _____

© 1992 by The Center for Applied Research in Education

WORD CIRCLES

/CH/ MEDIAL POSITION

FIND EVERY THIRD LETTER to find out what the puzzle says. Start at the arrow.

——— Say each word ——— times.
——— Learn the definition of each word.
——— Write a sentence for each word.
——— Make up a story using some of the words from the puzzle.
——— Draw pictures of some of the words from the puzzle.
——— Play "I Spy." Look around the classroom and find the words or the objects they represent.

——————— ————————————————————————————————— .

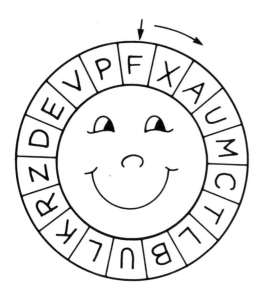

Answer: ————————————————

Answer: ————————————————

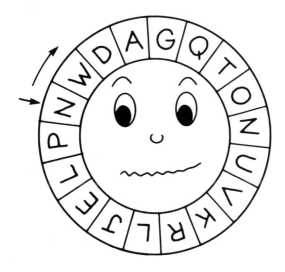

Answer: ————————————————

Answer: ————————————————

WORD CIRCLES

/CH/ FINAL POSITION

FIND EVERY THIRD LETTER to find out what the puzzle says. Start at the arrow.

_____ Say each word _____ times.
_____ Learn the definition of each word.
_____ Write a sentence for each word.
_____ Make up a story using some of the words from the puzzle.
_____ Draw pictures of some of the words from the puzzle.
_____ Play "I Spy." Look around the classroom and find the words or the objects they represent.

_____ _____ .

Answer: _____   Answer: _____

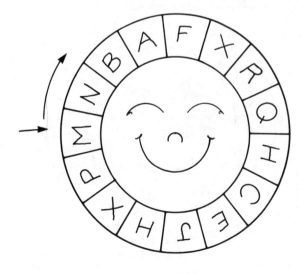

Answer: _____   Answer: _____

Name _____ Date _____

DOTTED WORDS

/CH/ INITIAL POSITION

COLOR THE DOTTED LETTERS to find the words.

_____ Say each word _____ times.
_____ Learn the definition of each word.
_____ Write a sentence for each word.
_____ Make up a story using one or both of the words from the puzzle.
_____ Draw pictures of one or both of the words from the puzzle.
_____ Play "I Spy." Look around the classroom and find the words or the objects they
        represent.

ANSWERS: _____ _____

Name _____ Date _____

DOTTED WORDS

/CH/ MEDIAL POSITION

COLOR THE DOTTED LETTERS to find the words.

_____ Say each word _____ times.
_____ Learn the definition of each word.
_____ Write a sentence for each word.
_____ Make up a story using one or both of the words from the puzzle.
_____ Draw pictures of one or both of the words from the puzzle.
_____ Play "I Spy." Look around the classroom and find the words or the objects they represent.

_____ _____ .

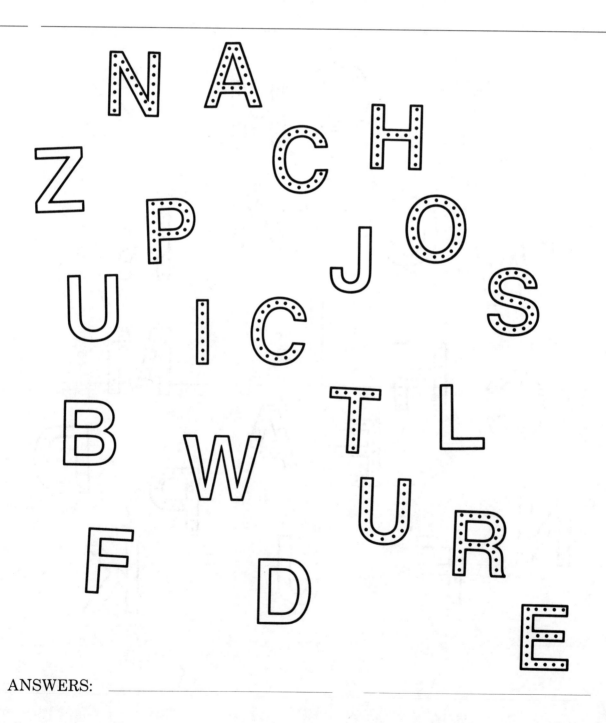

ANSWERS: _____

© 1992 by The Center for Applied Research in Education

DOTTED WORDS

/CH/ FINAL POSITION

COLOR THE DOTTED LETTERS to find the words.

_____ Say each word _____ times.
_____ Learn the definition of each word.
_____ Write a sentence for each word.
_____ Make up a story using one or both of the words from the puzzle.
_____ Draw pictures of one or both of the words from the puzzle.
_____ Play "I Spy." Look around the classroom and find the words or the objects they represent.

_____ _____ .

ANSWERS: _____   _____

SECRET CODES

/CH/ INITIAL POSITION

USE THE SECRET CODE TO SOLVE THE CODED WORDS. The answers are found at the bottom of this page in the Word Box.

_____ Say each word _____ times.
_____ Learn the definition of each word.
_____ Write a sentence for each word.
_____ Make up a story using some of the words from the puzzle.
_____ Draw pictures of some of the words from the puzzle.
_____ Play "I Spy." Look around the classroom and find the words or the objects they represent.

_____ _____ .

•SECRET CODE•

A	B	C	D	E	F	G	H	I	J	K
1	2	3	4	5	6	7	8	9	10	11
L	M	N	O	P	Q	R	S	T	U	V
12	13	14	15	16	17	18	19	20	21	22
W	X	Y	Z							
23	24	25	26							

---

1. 3 8 1 9 14
    __ __ __ __ __

2. 3 8 1 14 14 5 12
    __ __ __ __ __ __ __

3. 3 8 1 16 20 5 18
    __ __ __ __ __ __ __

4. 3 8 5 3 11
    __ __ __ __ __

5. 3 8 5 5 18
    __ __ __ __ __

6. 3 8 21 14 11
    __ __ __ __ __

7. 3 8 21 18 14
    __ __ __ __ __

8. 3 8 5 1 16
    __ __ __ __ __

9. 3 8 1 14 7 5
    __ __ __ __ __ __

10. 3 8 1 18 9 20 25
     __ __ __ __ __ __ __

•WORD BOX•

CHAIN	CHANNEL	CHARITY	CHECK	CHUNK
CHANGE	CHAPTER	CHEAP	CHEER	CHURN

SECRET CODES

/CH/ MEDIAL POSITION

USE THE SECRET CODE TO SOLVE THE CODED WORDS. The answers are found at the bottom of this page in the Word Box.

_____ Say each word _____ times.
_____ Learn the definition of each word.
_____ Write a sentence for each word.
_____ Make up a story using some of the words from the puzzle.
_____ Draw pictures of some of the words from the puzzle.
_____ Play "I Spy." Look around the classroom and find the words or the objects they represent.

_____ _____ .

•SECRET CODE•

A	B	C	D	E	F	G	H	I	J	K
1	2	3	4	5	6	7	8	9	10	11
L	M	N	O	P	Q	R	S	T	U	V
12	13	14	15	16	17	18	19	20	21	22
W	X	Y	Z							
23	24	25	26							

1. 4   5   14   20   21   18   5   19

_   _   _   _   _   _   _   _

2. 17   21   5   19   20   9   15   14

_   _   _   _   _   _   _   _

3. 19   20   1   20   21   5

_   _   _   _   _   _

4. 1   4   22   5   14   20   21   18   5

_   _   _   _   _   _   _   _   _

5. 13   21   20   21   1   12

_   _   _   _   _   _

6. 18   5   1   3   8   9   14   7

_   _   _   _   _   _   _   _

7. 16   9   3   20   21   18   5

_   _   _   _   _   _   _

8. 3   21   12   20   21   18   5

_   _   _   _   _   _   _

9. 20   5   24   20   21   18   5

_   _   _   _   _   _   _

10. 6   5   1   20   21   18   5

_   _   _   _   _   _   _

•WORD BOX•

ADVENTURE	DENTURES	MUTUAL	QUESTION	STATUE
CULTURE	FEATURE	PICTURE	REACHING	TEXTURE

Name _____   Date _____

SECRET CODES

/CH/ FINAL POSITION

USE THE SECRET CODE TO SOLVE THE CODED WORDS. The answers are found at the bottom of this page in the Word Box.

_____ Say each word _____ times.
_____ Learn the definition of each word.
_____ Write a sentence for each word.
_____ Make up a story using some of the words from the puzzle.
_____ Draw pictures of some of the words from the puzzle.
_____ Play "I Spy." Look around the classroom and find the words or the objects they represent.

_____ _____ .

•SECRET CODE•

A	B	C	D	E	F	G	H	I	J	K
1	2	3	4	5	6	7	8	9	10	11
L	M	N	O	P	Q	R	S	T	U	V
12	13	14	15	16	17	18	19	20	21	22
W	X	Y	Z							
23	24	25	26							

---

1. 12 1 20 3 8
    __ __ __ __ __

2. 7 18 15 21 3 8
    __ __ __ __ __ __

3. 1 16 16 18 15 1 3 8
    __ __ __ __ __ __ __ __

4. 23 18 5 14 3 8
    __ __ __ __ __ __

5. 19 20 18 5 20 3 8
    __ __ __ __ __ __ __

6. 1 20 20 1 3 8
    __ __ __ __ __ __

7. 19 20 9 20 3 8
    __ __ __ __ __ __

8. 3 15 21 3 8
    __ __ __ __ __

9. 16 1 20 3 8
    __ __ __ __ __

10. 15 21 3 8
     __ __ __ __

•WORD BOX•

APPROACH	COUCH	LATCH	PATCH	STRETCH
ATTACH	GROUCH	OUCH	STITCH	WRENCH

© 1992 by The Center for Applied Research in Education

Name _____ Date _____

SCRAMBLED WORDS

/CH/ INITIAL POSITION

UNSCRAMBLE THE WORDS. The answers are in the Word Box.

_____ Say each word _____ times.
_____ Learn the definition of each word.
_____ Write a sentence for each word.
_____ Make up a story using some of the words from the puzzle.
_____ Draw pictures of some of the words from the puzzle.
_____ Play "I Spy." Look around the classroom and find the words or the objects they represent.

_____ _____ .

1. CHNCAE _____
2. ECOHK _____
3. CCHKEERS _____
4. NIHC _____
5. YCLHLI _____
6. RAHCITY _____
7. ACHT _____
8. EATCH _____
9. KOOBKCEHC _____
10. PTAHRCE _____
11. SSCHE _____
12. UHCCRH _____
13. HESEEC _____
14. REIEHSCR _____
15. EONSCH _____

•WORD BOX•				
CHANCE	CHAT	CHECKERS	CHILLY	CHOKE
CHAPTER	CHEAT	CHEESE	CHESS	CHOSEN
CHARITY	CHECKBOOK	CHERRIES	CHIN	CHURCH

Name _____ Date _____

SCRAMBLED WORDS

/CH/ MEDIAL POSITION

UNSCRAMBLE THE WORDS. The answers are in the Word Box.

_____ Say each word _____ times.
_____ Learn the definition of each word.
_____ Write a sentence for each word.
_____ Make up a story using some of the words from the puzzle.
_____ Draw pictures of some of the words from the puzzle.
_____ Play "I Spy." Look around the classroom and find the words or the objects they
represent.

_____ _____ .

1. VDATNEERU   _____

2. CWAIHGNT   _____

3. CKTEHNI   _____

4. LEERCUT   _____

5. CIRAEHGN   _____

6. TIREUCP   _____

7. RRAMAIHC   _____

8. UFRTNRUEI   _____

9. BBLLAACHE   _____

10. CETAUERR   _____

11. CIGARNDHLD   _____

12. HEESPAC   _____

13. RTEUUF   _____

14. GNIHCAET   _____

15. BUTREHC   _____

•WORD BOX•

ADVENTURE	BUTCHER	FUTURE	LECTURE	REACHING
ARMCHAIR	CREATURE	GRANDCHILD	PEACHES	TEACHING
BEACHBALL	FURNITURE	KITCHEN	PICTURE	WATCHING

SCRAMBLED WORDS

/CH/ FINAL POSITION

UNSCRAMBLE THE WORDS. The answers are in the Word Box.

_____ Say each word _____ times.
_____ Learn the definition of each word.
_____ Write a sentence for each word.
_____ Make up a story using some of the words from the puzzle.
_____ Draw pictures of some of the words from the puzzle.
_____ Play "I Spy." Look around the classroom and find the words or the objects they represent.

1. PEACHR   _____
2. TCHAAT   _____
3. HCNARB   _____
4. SCHOOPTCH   _____
5. THCEF   _____
6. RSACCHT   _____
7. UOTCH   _____
8. ICTHD   _____
9. LHCUN   _____
10. HCAE   _____
11. CHBLAE   _____
12. CCTAH   _____
13. WDASINHC   _____
14. TOSIRCH   _____
15. HCNAR   _____

•WORD BOX•				
ATTACH	CATCH	FETCH	OSTRICH	SANDWICH
BLEACH	DITCH	HOPSCOTCH	PREACH	SCRATCH
BRANCH	EACH	LUNCH	RANCH	TOUCH

Name _____   Date _____

WORD FIND

/CH/ INITIAL POSITION

FIND THE WORDS IN THE WORD BOX THAT ARE HIDDEN IN THE PUZZLE. They may be hidden down, across, upside down, diagonal, or backwards.

_____ Say each word _____ times.
_____ Learn the definition of each word.
_____ Write a sentence for each word.
_____ Make up a story using some of the words from the puzzle.
_____ Draw pictures of some of the words from the puzzle.
_____ Play "I Spy." Look around the classroom and find the words or the objects they represent.

_____ _____ .

```
V   L   H   C   H   E   S   S   E   C   M
R   C   C   H   G   D   R   C   C   H   O
M   H   R   J   U   I   C   H   I   L   D
E   I   U   C   A   H   W   E   O   C   P
G   C   H   H   A   C   H   A   H   H   X
N   K   C   P   T   H   C   P   C   O   B
A   Q   C   H   E   C   K   E   R   S   C
H   C   K   C   H   E   E   S   E   E   H
C   S   F   N   I   H   C   D   X   N   M
C   H   E   R   R   Y   C   H   I   L   L
```

•WORD BOX•		
CHAIR	CHEESE	CHILL
CHANGE	CHERRY	CHIN
CHAP	CHESS	CHOICE
CHEAP	CHICK	CHOSEN
CHECKERS	CHILD	CHURCH

WORD FIND

/CH/ MEDIAL POSITION

FIND THE WORDS IN THE WORD BOX THAT ARE HIDDEN IN THE PUZZLE. They
may be hidden down, across, upside down, diagonal, or backwards.

_____ Say each word _____ times.
_____ Learn the definition of each word.
_____ Write a sentence for each word.
_____ Make up a story using some of the words from the puzzle.
_____ Draw pictures of some of the words from the puzzle.
_____ Play "I Spy." Look around the classroom and find the words or the objects they
represent.

```
A  P  I  T  C  H  E  R  R  C  H  V
M  A  V  A  M  N  C  I  O  R  T  C
A  S  L  O  A  C  A  C  E  H  E  S
T  T  P  T  X  H  M  H  Q  A  A  N
C  U  U  B  C  L  C  G  H  P  C  E
H  R  U  M  P  T  L  E  A  I  H  H
E  E  R  D  U  A  Y  S  S  C  E  C
S  A  C  B  R  N  T  T  C  T  R  T
V  N  L  U  H  U  K  U  R  U  P  I
O  Q  T  E  R  F  N  R  W  R  D  K
F  A  F  U  T  U  R  E  Z  E  X  C
N  G  S  E  H  C  A  O  R  J  M  G
H  C  R  E  H  C  A  E  R  P  B  J
```

•WORD BOX•

ARMCHAIR	MATCHES	PITCHER
BUTCHER	NATURAL	PREACHER
FUTURE	NATURE	ROACHES
GESTURE	PASTURE	TEACHER
KITCHEN	PICTURE	

WORD FIND

/CH/ FINAL POSITION

FIND THE WORDS IN THE WORD BOX THAT ARE HIDDEN IN THE PUZZLE. They
may be hidden down, across, upside down, diagonal, or backwards.

_____ Say each word _____ times.
_____ Learn the definition of each word.
_____ Write a sentence for each word.
_____ Make up a story using some of the words from the puzzle.
_____ Draw pictures of some of the words from the puzzle.
_____ Play "I Spy." Look around the classroom and find the words or the objects they
represent.

_____ _____ .

```
X  F  B  W  I  T  C  H  X  I  O
M  G  S  T  I  T  C  H  H  H  P
L  H  V  A  D  A  U  H  C  C  E
F  C  S  P  E  E  C  H  U  H  A
H  N  D  B  H  I  F  Y  S  C  C
C  U  M  C  W  H  I  C  H  A  H
A  L  U  H  C  U  M  D  Z  E  B
E  O  Q  D  I  T  C  H  J  R  G
T  S  A  N  D  W  I  C  H  P  N
C  H  C  T  I  W  S  N  E  J  K
```

•WORD BOX•		
BEACH	PREACH	SWITCH
DITCH	SANDWICH	TEACH
LUNCH	SPEECH	TOUCH
MUCH	STITCH	WHICH
PEACH	SUCH	WITCH

Name _____   Date _____

CROSSWORD PUZZLE

/CH/ INITIAL POSITION

COMPLETE THE PUZZLE. The answers are in the Word Box.

_____ Say each word _____ times.
_____ Learn the definition of each word.
_____ Write a sentence for each word.
_____ Make up a story using some of the words from the puzzle.
_____ Draw pictures of some of the words from the puzzle.
_____ Play "I Spy." Look around the classroom and find the words or the objects they represent.

_____ _____ .

•WORD BOX•

CHAIRMAN	CHECKERS	CHESS	CHIN	CHOOSE
CHEAP	CHEESE	CHILDREN	CHINA	CHOP
CHECK	CHERRY	CHIMNEY	CHIPMUNKS	

ACROSS
1. Head of a committee
3. Fruit flavor
4. Cut
5. Board game with round objects
7. Pressed curd of milk
9. Inexpensive
10. End of face

DOWN
1. To decide
2. Board game with different-shaped objects
5. To mark
6. Smoke flue
7. Sons and daughters
8. Alvin and the _____
9. Dishes

Name _____   Date _____

CROSSWORD PUZZLE

/CH/ MEDIAL POSITION

COMPLETE THE PUZZLE. The answers are in the Word Box.

_____ Say each word _____ times.
_____ Learn the definition of each word.
_____ Write a sentence for each word.
_____ Make up a story using some of the words from the puzzle.
_____ Draw pictures of some of the words from the puzzle.
_____ Play "I Spy." Look around the classroom and find the words or the objects they
represent.

_____ .

•WORD BOX•				
AMATEUR	CREATURE	GRANDCHILD	LUNCHROOM	SEARCHING
ARMCHAIR	ETCHES	INCHES	SATCHEL	WITCHES
BEACHBALL	GESTURE	LECTURE		

ACROSS
1. My son's son
5. Drawings
8. To admonish
9. Movement
11. Easy chair
12. Evil women
13. Cafeteria

DOWN
2. Unprofessional
3. Monster
4. Measurement of size
6. Bag
7. Round toy used in the water
10. Looking

Name _____ Date _____

CROSSWORD PUZZLE

/CH/ FINAL POSITION

COMPLETE THE PUZZLE. The answers are in the Word Box.

_____ Say each word _____ times.
_____ Learn the definition of each word.
_____ Write a sentence for each word.
_____ Make up a story using some of the words from the puzzle.
_____ Draw pictures of some of the words from the puzzle.
_____ Play "I Spy." Look around the classroom and find the words or the objects they represent.

_____ _____ .

•WORD BOX•

APPROACH	COCKROACH	ITCH	PITCH	TEACH
AVALANCHE	COUCH	LATCH	RANCH	WATCH
BENCH	EACH	OSTRICH	SPEECH	WRENCH
COACH	HOPSCOTCH			

ACROSS

1. To come closer
5. To lock
6. A type of bug
8. To train
10. Tool
11. It causes you to scratch
13. Timepiece
14. To help someone learn
15. To throw

DOWN

1. A large snowslide
2. A cattle farm
3. Sofa
4. Every one
7. A large bird
9. A sidewalk game
12. A long seat

ACTIVITIES FOR /D/

21

Name _____   Date _____

WORD CIRCLES

/D/ INITIAL POSITION

FIND EVERY THIRD LETTER to find out what the puzzle says. Start at the arrow.

_____ Say each word _____ times.
_____ Learn the definition of each word.
_____ Write a sentence for each word.
_____ Make up a story using some of the words from the puzzle.
_____ Draw pictures of some of the words from the puzzle.
_____ Play "I Spy." Look around the classroom and find the words or the objects they represent.

_____ _____ .

Answer: _____   Answer: _____

Answer: _____   Answer: _____

Name _____ Date _____

WORD CIRCLES

/D/ MEDIAL POSITION

FIND EVERY THIRD LETTER to find out what the puzzle says. Start at the arrow.

_____ Say each word _____ times.
_____ Learn the definition of each word.
_____ Write a sentence for each word.
_____ Make up a story using some of the words from the puzzle.
_____ Draw pictures of some of the words from the puzzle.
_____ Play "I Spy." Look around the classroom and find the words or the objects they represent.

_____ _____ .

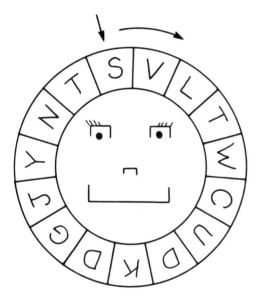

Answer: _____

Answer: _____

Answer: _____

Answer: _____

WORD CIRCLES

/D/ FINAL POSITION

FIND EVERY THIRD LETTER to find out what the puzzle says. Start at the arrow.

_____ Say each word _____ times.
_____ Learn the definition of each word.
_____ Write a sentence for each word.
_____ Make up a story using some of the words from the puzzle.
_____ Draw pictures of some of the words from the puzzle.
_____ Play "I Spy." Look around the classroom and find the words or the objects they represent.

_____ _____ .

Answer:_____   Answer:_____

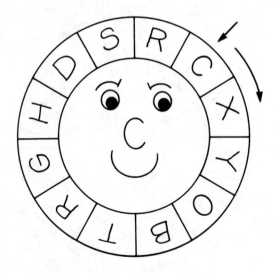

Answer:_____   Answer:_____

Name _____ Date _____

DOTTED WORDS

/D/ **INITIAL POSITION**

COLOR THE DOTTED LETTERS to find the words.

_____ Say each word _____ times.
_____ Learn the definition of each word.
_____ Write a sentence for each word.
_____ Make up a story using one or both of the words from the puzzle.
_____ Draw pictures of one or both of the words from the puzzle.
_____ Play "I Spy." Look around the classroom and find the words or the objects they represent.

_____ _____ .

ANSWERS: _____

Name _____ Date _____

DOTTED WORDS

/D/ MEDIAL POSITION

COLOR THE DOTTED LETTERS to find the words.

_____ Say each word _____ times.
_____ Learn the definition of each word.
_____ Write a sentence for each word.
_____ Make up a story using one or both of the words from the puzzle.
_____ Draw pictures of one or both of the words from the puzzle.
_____ Play "I Spy." Look around the classroom and find the words or the objects they
represent.

_____ _____ .

ANSWERS: _____ _____

DOTTED WORDS

/D/ FINAL POSITION

COLOR THE DOTTED LETTERS to find the words.

_____ Say each word _____ times.
_____ Learn the definition of each word.
_____ Write a sentence for each word.
_____ Make up a story using one or both of the words from the puzzle.
_____ Draw pictures of one or both of the words from the puzzle.
_____ Play "I Spy." Look around the classroom and find the words or the objects they
        represent.

_____ _____ .

ANSWERS: _____   _____

SECRET CODES

/D/ INITIAL POSITION

USE THE SECRET CODE TO SOLVE THE CODED WORDS. The answers are found at the bottom of this page in the Word Box.

_____ Say each word _____ times.
_____ Learn the definition of each word.
_____ Write a sentence for each word.
_____ Make up a story using some of the words from the puzzle.
_____ Draw pictures of some of the words from the puzzle.
_____ Play "I Spy." Look around the classroom and find the words or the objects they represent.

_____ _____ .

```
•SECRET CODE•
A     B     C     D     E     F     G     H     I     J     K
5     10    15    20    25    30    35    40    45    50    55
L     M     N     O     P     Q     R     S     T     U     V
60    65    70    75    80    85    90    95    100   105   110
W     X     Y     Z
115   120   125   130
```

1. 20   5   115   70
    __ __ __   __

6. 20   5   70   20   90   105   30   30
    __ __ __   __   __   __   __   __

2. 20   75   105   10   60   25
    __ __   __   __   __   __

7. 20   75   130   25   70
    __ __   __   __   __

3. 20   25   30   25   5   100
    __ __   __   __   __ __

8. 20   45   130   130   125
    __ __   __   __   __

4. 20   45   95   65   45   95   95
    __ __   __   __   __   __   __

9. 20   25   70   45   5   60
    __ __   __   __ __ __

5. 20   105   25   100
    __ __   __   __

10. 20   5   70   15   25
    __ __ __   __   __

```
•WORD BOX•
DANCE        DAWN        DENIAL       DIZZY        DOZEN
DANDRUFF     DEFEAT      DISMISS      DOUBLE       DUET
```

SECRET CODES

/D/ MEDIAL POSITION

USE THE SECRET CODE TO SOLVE THE CODED WORDS. The answers are found at the bottom of this page in the Word Box.

_____ Say each word _____ times.
_____ Learn the definition of each word.
_____ Write a sentence for each word.
_____ Make up a story using some of the words from the puzzle.
_____ Draw pictures of some of the words from the puzzle.
_____ Play "I Spy." Look around the classroom and find the words or the objects they represent.

_____ _____ .

•SECRET CODE•

A	B	C	D	E	F	G	H	I	J	K
5	10	15	20	25	30	35	40	45	50	55
L	M	N	O	P	Q	R	S	T	U	V
60	65	70	75	80	85	90	95	100	105	110
W	X	Y	Z							
115	120	125	130							

1. 75 20 75 90 75 105 95
   __ __ __ __ __ __ __

2. 90 45 20 25 90
   __ __ __ __ __

3. 90 75 20 25 75
   __ __ __ __ __

4. 65 25 20 45 15 45 70 25
   __ __ __ __ __ __ __ __

5. 65 25 20 45 5 60
   __ __ __ __ __ __

6. 100 45 20 125
   __ __ __ __

7. 110 5 70 20 5 60 95
   __ __ __ __ __ __ __

8. 40 25 5 20 5 15 40 25
   __ __ __ __ __ __ __ __

9. 40 45 20 20 25 70
   __ __ __ __ __ __

10. 95 40 105 20 20 25 90
    __ __ __ __ __ __ __

•WORD BOX•

HEADACHE	MEDIAL	ODOROUS	RODEO	TIDY
HIDDEN	MEDICINE	RIDER	SHUDDER	VANDALS

SECRET CODES

/D/ FINAL POSITION

USE THE SECRET CODE TO SOLVE THE CODED WORDS. The answers are found at the bottom of this page in the Word Box.

_____ Say each word _____ times.
_____ Learn the definition of each word.
_____ Write a sentence for each word.
_____ Make up a story using some of the words from the puzzle.
_____ Draw pictures of some of the words from the puzzle.
_____ Play "I Spy." Look around the classroom and find the words or the objects they represent.

_____ _____ .

•SECRET CODE•										
A	B	C	D	E	F	G	H	I	J	K
5	10	15	20	25	30	35	40	45	50	55
L	M	N	O	P	Q	R	S	T	U	V
60	65	70	75	80	85	90	95	100	105	110
W	X	Y	Z							
115	120	125	130							

1. 60 25 65 75 70 5 20 25
    ___ ___ ___ ___ ___ ___ ___ ___

2. 5 45 20 25 20
    ___ ___ ___ ___ ___

3. 95 80 75 100 100 25 20
    ___ ___ ___ ___ ___ ___ ___

4. 65 75 110 25 20
    ___ ___ ___ ___ ___

5. 70 25 25 20 25 20
    ___ ___ ___ ___ ___ ___

6. 115 45 20 25
    ___ ___ ___ ___

7. 15 75 105 60 20
    ___ ___ ___ ___ ___

8. 100 90 45 25 20
    ___ ___ ___ ___ ___

9. 95 40 5 20 25
    ___ ___ ___ ___ ___

10. 10 90 25 5 20
    ___ ___ ___ ___ ___

•WORD BOX•				
AIDED	COULD	MOVED	SHADE	TRIED
BREAD	LEMONADE	NEEDED	SPOTTED	WIDE

SCRAMBLED WORDS

/D/ INITIAL POSITION

UNSCRAMBLE THE WORDS. The answers are in the Word Box.

_____ Say each word _____ times.
_____ Learn the definition of each word.
_____ Write a sentence for each word.
_____ Make up a story using some of the words from the puzzle.
_____ Draw pictures of some of the words from the puzzle.
_____ Play "I Spy." Look around the classroom and find the words or the objects they represent.

_____ _____ .

1. YSCEIOVRD   _____

2. DOUAINSR   _____

3. DLAI   _____

4. TNECED   _____

5. YDRIA   _____

6. SSEDERT   _____

7. SEDERT   _____

8. FFEERNTID   _____

9. DLCTEIAE   _____

10. DYA   _____

11. DDECIE   _____

12. EEDP   _____

13. CCRYAOMED   _____

14. TEID   _____

15. ERNGDA   _____

•WORD BOX•

DAIRY	DECENT	DELICATE	DESSERT	DIFFERENT
DANGER	DECIDE	DEMOCRACY	DIAL	DINOSAUR
DAY	DEEP	DESERT	DIET	DISCOVERY

SCRAMBLED WORDS

/D/ MEDIAL POSITION

UNSCRAMBLE THE WORDS. The answers are in the Word Box.

_____ Say each word _____ times.
_____ Learn the definition of each word.
_____ Write a sentence for each word.
_____ Make up a story using some of the words from the puzzle.
_____ Draw pictures of some of the words from the puzzle.
_____ Play "I Spy." Look around the classroom and find the words or the objects they
         represent.

_____ _____.

1. YDLA   _____

2. OODR   _____

3. DDDAY   _____

4. FDNGEEI   _____

5. IICNEDEM   _____

6. TDYOA   _____

7. OIARD   _____

8. GOD TOH   _____

9. WPDROE   _____

10. SPDREI   _____

11. DRRAA   _____

12. REDWCHO   _____

13. YBAIDRTH   _____

14. BDYO   _____

15. LARDED   _____

•WORD BOX•				
BIRTHDAY	DADDY	LADDER	ODOR	RADIO
BODY	FEEDING	LADY	POWDER	SPIDER
CHOWDER	HOT DOG	MEDICINE	RADAR	TODAY

SCRAMBLED WORDS

/D/ FINAL POSITION

UNSCRAMBLE THE WORDS. The answers are in the Word Box.

_____ Say each word _____ times.
_____ Learn the definition of each word.
_____ Write a sentence for each word.
_____ Make up a story using some of the words from the puzzle.
_____ Draw pictures of some of the words from the puzzle.
_____ Play "I Spy." Look around the classroom and find the words or the objects they represent.

_____ _____ .

1. CLDUO   _____

2. DIHE   _____

3. LEID   _____

4. AD   _____

5. CDEIR   _____

6. TEID   _____

7. OODF   _____

8. DAH   _____

9. EDAB   _____

10. RBAED   _____

11. RRDLAIOA   _____

12. GGDDRAE   _____

13. ASLAD   _____

14. HAAED   _____

15. DEB   _____

•WORD BOX•

AD	BED	CRIED	HAD	RAILROAD
AHEAD	BREAD	DRAGGED	HIDE	SALAD
BEAD	COULD	FOOD	LIED	TIDE

WORD FIND

/D/ INITIAL POSITION

FIND THE WORDS IN THE WORD BOX THAT ARE HIDDEN IN THE PUZZLE. They
may be hidden down, across, upside down, diagonal, or backwards.

_____ Say each word _____ times.
_____ Learn the definition of each word.
_____ Write a sentence for each word.
_____ Make up a story using some of the words from the puzzle.
_____ Draw pictures of some of the words from the puzzle.
_____ Play "I Spy." Look around the classroom and find the words or the objects they
represent.

_____ _____ .

```
T  J  Y  B  F  O  Z  G  C  K  P  Y  M  L  Q
D  D  D  E  L  I  C  A  T  E  T  V  D  G  D
E  D  O  U  B  L  E  P  M  R  U  K  Y  X  I
S  D  D  U  C  K  D  D  I  W  D  T  R  U  C
T  A  I  M  R  S  D  D  T  C  K  D  A  E  T
I  L  D  Q  F  U  M  D  O  Z  E  N  I  D  I
N  Z  N  P  M  E  Z  R  E  P  A  I  D  L  O
A  T  W  B  X  C  W  D  G  O  Q  H  T  L  N
T  V  O  Z  U  R  M  D  E  S  S  E  R  T  A
I  X  D  L  N  D  F  Y  P  X  J  D  S  D  R
O  F  T  M  V  E  S  A  E  S  I  D  W  D  Y
N  E  M  D  I  F  F  I  C  U  L  T  K  Z  B
```

+---+
| •WORD BOX• |
| DELICATE   DICTIONARY   DOUBLE |
| DESSERT   DID   DOWN |
| DESTINATION   DIFFICULT   DOZEN |
| DIAPER   DIRTY   DUCK |
| DIARY   DISEASE   DUMB |
+---+

Name _____   Date _____

WORD FIND

/D/ MEDIAL POSITION

FIND THE WORDS IN THE WORD BOX THAT ARE HIDDEN IN THE PUZZLE. They may be hidden down, across, upside down, diagonal, or backwards.

_____ Say each word _____ times.
_____ Learn the definition of each word.
_____ Write a sentence for each word.
_____ Make up a story using some of the words from the puzzle.
_____ Draw pictures of some of the words from the puzzle.
_____ Play "I Spy." Look around the classroom and find the words or the objects they represent.

_____ _____ .

```
D  D  L  S  P  I  D  E  R  P  D  Y  B  G  Q
D  D  N  E  D  D  I  H  N  O  S  F  M  V  T
A  V  O  C  A  D  O  E  X  D  K  H  C  B  E
M  M  F  L  P  L  M  Q  I  Q  R  M  G  X  D
Q  Y  K  D  B  O  Z  O  A  Y  E  S  N  I  I
N  D  P  W  D  E  N  J  V  A  L  J  I  D  O
Y  O  V  B  D  E  Q  D  D  T  R  U  D  K  U
F  B  A  D  D  R  D  O  D  Z  E  H  D  M  S
A  O  K  A  E  C  W  F  T  I  D  Y  A  N  L
J  N  B  D  B  D  N  R  H  G  I  C  Y  G  M
Q  J  I  I  Y  D  O  B  K  O  R  Z  R  L  D
V  L  P  O  W  D  E  R  P  H  N  E  W  Y  S
G  D  X  U  E  N  I  C  I  D  E  M  J  T  D
```

•WORD BOX•

ABDOMEN	GLIDER	POWDER
ADDING	HIDDEN	RIDER
ADENOIDS	MEADOW	SPIDER
AVOCADO	MEDICINE	TEDIOUS
BODY	NOBODY	TIDY

Name _____   Date _____

WORD FIND

/D/ FINAL POSITION

FIND THE WORDS IN THE WORD BOX THAT ARE HIDDEN IN THE PUZZLE. They
may be hidden down, across, upside down, diagonal, or backwards.

_____ Say each word _____ times.
_____ Learn the definition of each word.
_____ Write a sentence for each word.
_____ Make up a story using some of the words from the puzzle.
_____ Draw pictures of some of the words from the puzzle.
_____ Play "I Spy." Look around the classroom and find the words or the objects they
      represent.

_____ _____ .

```
D  D  S  P  Z  F  Q  K  W  O  O  D  L  V  M
D  E  D  K  C  R  O  W  D  E  D  G  O  P  P
D  D  E  M  P  D  X  Q  B  N  Y  D  D  D  D
T  E  T  W  D  J  E  D  A  R  G  E  A  D  Q
Z  E  N  I  E  K  N  R  L  X  B  O  F  D  Z
F  N  I  D  T  D  L  U  O  W  R  Z  C  S  R
B  D  A  E  A  M  D  W  H  L  C  A  G  E  Y
J  A  P  D  H  A  D  O  I  D  R  T  J  E  X
L  S  T  U  L  D  D  A  Z  C  U  D  X  D  C
T  I  D  T  P  N  R  K  A  F  T  O  A  D  D
V  D  O  Q  E  D  R  D  E  S  D  V  P  Y  F
Y  E  W  D  U  D  E  T  D  M  D  X  D  K  L
```

<table>
<tr><td colspan="3" align="center">•WORD BOX•</td></tr>
<tr><td>ARCADE</td><td>HATED</td><td>SIDE</td></tr>
<tr><td>BATTED</td><td>NEEDED</td><td>TOAD</td></tr>
<tr><td>CROWDED</td><td>PAINTED</td><td>WIDE</td></tr>
<tr><td>GRADE</td><td>RAILROAD</td><td>WOOD</td></tr>
<tr><td>HAD</td><td>SEED</td><td>WOULD</td></tr>
</table>

Name _____ Date _____

CROSSWORD PUZZLE

/D/ INITIAL POSITION

COMPLETE THE PUZZLE. The answers are in the Word Box.

_____ Say each word _____ times.
_____ Learn the definition of each word.
_____ Write a sentence for each word.
_____ Make up a story using some of the words from the puzzle.
_____ Draw pictures of some of the words from the puzzle.
_____ Play "I Spy." Look around the classroom and find the words or the objects they represent.

_____ .

•WORD BOX•

DADDY LONG LEGS	DAWN	DEAF	DEMAND	DOCTOR
DANDELION	DEAL	DEEP	DIAMOND	DOLL
DANGER	DEBTOR	DEFECTIVE	DIGEST	DOWN

ACROSS
2. When morning breaks
3. A type of spider
6. To ask for
8. Peril
9. Broken
10. One who owes money
11. A bargain

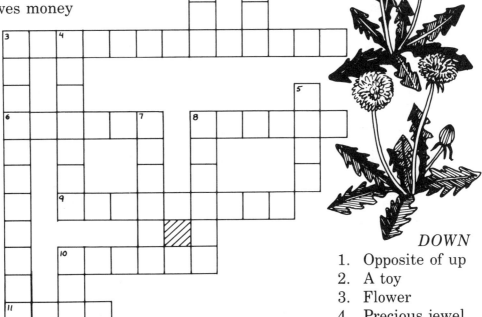

DOWN
1. Opposite of up
2. A toy
3. Flower
4. Precious jewel
5. Not shallow
7. To absorb food
8. Physician
10. Not being able to hear

CROSSWORD PUZZLE

/D/ MEDIAL POSITION

COMPLETE THE PUZZLE. The answers are in the Word Box.

_____ Say each word _____ times.
_____ Learn the definition of each word.
_____ Write a sentence for each word.
_____ Make up a story using some of the words from the puzzle.
_____ Draw pictures of some of the words from the puzzle.
_____ Play "I Spy." Look around the classroom and find the words or the objects they represent.

_____ _____ .

•WORD BOX•

BIDDY	LADDER	MEDICINE	ODOR	TODAY
BIRTHDAY	LADY	NEEDLE	SPIDER	TODDLER
KINDERGARTEN	MEADOW			

ACROSS
4. Eight-legged insect
5. Sharp instrument
7. A doctor prescribes this
8. A hen
9. This day
10. A gracious woman

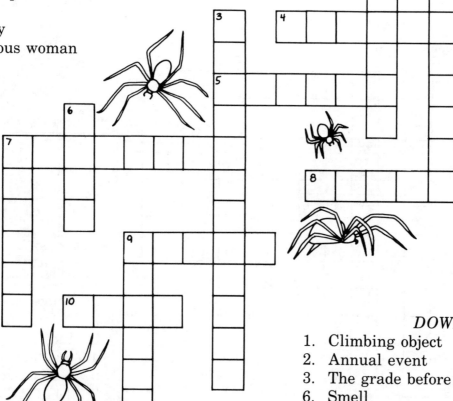

DOWN
1. Climbing object
2. Annual event
3. The grade before first grade
6. Smell
7. Flat grassy land
9. A baby just beginning to walk

© 1989 by The Center for Applied Research in Education

CROSSWORD PUZZLE

/D/ FINAL POSITION

COMPLETE THE PUZZLE. The answers are in the Word Box.

_____ Say each word _____ times.
_____ Learn the definition of each word.
_____ Write a sentence for each word.
_____ Make up a story using some of the words from the puzzle.
_____ Draw pictures of some of the words from the puzzle.
_____ Play "I Spy." Look around the classroom and find the words or the objects they represent.

_____ _____ .

•WORD BOX•

AROUND	GUIDE	NEIGHBORHOOD	PRETEND	ROAD
ASCEND	HERD	OLD	RED	ROD
COD	MAD	PERSUADE	RIDE	WOOD
DREAD	MADE			

ACROSS
1. To go in circles
5. A type of fish
6. To act
7. A path for cars
9. Color
10. A leader
11. Tree material
12. Angry
13. A group of cattle
14. A pole

DOWN
1. To go up
2. Not young
3. An area of houses
4. To travel in a vehicle
6. To influence
8. Anxious
12. Past tense of make

ACTIVITIES FOR /F/

Name _____   Date _____

WORD CIRCLES

/F/ INITIAL POSITION

FIND EVERY THIRD LETTER to find out what the puzzle says. Start at the arrow.

_____ Say each word _____ times.
_____ Learn the definition of each word.
_____ Write a sentence for each word.
_____ Make up a story using some of the words from the puzzle.
_____ Draw pictures of some of the words from the puzzle.
_____ Play "I Spy." Look around the classroom and find the words or the objects they
represent.

_____ _____ .

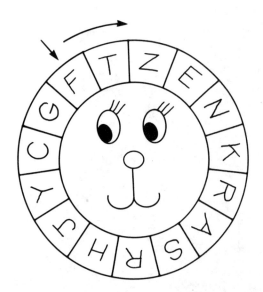

Answer: _____

Answer: _____

Answer: _____

Answer: _____

WORD CIRCLES

/F/ MEDIAL POSITION

FIND EVERY THIRD LETTER to find out what the puzzle says. Start at the arrow.

_____ Say each word _____ times.
_____ Learn the definition of each word.
_____ Write a sentence for each word.
_____ Make up a story using some of the words from the puzzle.
_____ Draw pictures of some of the words from the puzzle.
_____ Play "I Spy." Look around the classroom and find the words or the objects they
_____ represent.

_____ _____ .

Answer:_____

Answer:_____

Answer:_____

Answer:_____

WORD CIRCLES

/F/   FINAL POSITION

FIND EVERY THIRD LETTER to find out what the puzzle says. Start at the arrow.

_____ Say each word _____ times.
_____ Learn the definition of each word.
_____ Write a sentence for each word.
_____ Make up a story using some of the words from the puzzle.
_____ Draw pictures of some of the words from the puzzle.
_____ Play "I Spy." Look around the classroom and find the words or the objects they
represent.

_____ _____ .

Answer: _____

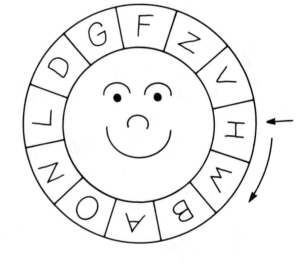

Answer: _____

Answer: _____

Answer: _____

Name _____ Date _____

DOTTED WORDS

/F/ INITIAL POSITION

COLOR THE DOTTED LETTERS to find the words.

_____ Say each word _____ times.
_____ Learn the definition of each word.
_____ Write a sentence for each word.
_____ Make up a story using one or both of the words from the puzzle.
_____ Draw pictures of one or both of the words from the puzzle.
_____ Play "I Spy." Look around the classroom and find the words or the objects they represent.

_____ .

ANSWERS: _____ _____

Name _____ Date _____

DOTTED WORDS

/F/ **MEDIAL POSITION**

COLOR THE DOTTED LETTERS to find the words.

_____ Say each word _____ times.
_____ Learn the definition of each word.
_____ Write a sentence for each word.
_____ Make up a story using one or both of the words from the puzzle.
_____ Draw pictures of one or both of the words from the puzzle.
_____ Play "I Spy." Look around the classroom and find the words or the objects they represent.

_____ _____ .

ANSWERS: _____ _____

Name _____   Date _____

DOTTED WORDS

/F/ FINAL POSITION

COLOR THE DOTTED LETTERS to find the words.

_____ Say each word _____ times.
_____ Learn the definition of each word.
_____ Write a sentence for each word.
_____ Make up a story using one or both of the words from the puzzle.
_____ Draw pictures of one or both of the words from the puzzle.
_____ Play "I Spy." Look around the classroom and find the words or the objects they represent.

_____ _____ .

ANSWERS: _____   _____

Name _____   Date _____

SECRET CODES

/F/ INITIAL POSITION

USE THE SECRET CODE TO SOLVE THE CODED WORDS. The answers are found at the bottom of this page in the Word Box.

_____ Say each word _____ times.
_____ Learn the definition of each word.
_____ Write a sentence for each word.
_____ Make up a story using some of the words from the puzzle.
_____ Draw pictures of some of the words from the puzzle.
_____ Play "I Spy." Look around the classroom and find the words or the objects they
represent.

_____ _____ .

```
•SECRET CODE•

A    B    C    D    E    F    G    H    I    J    K
1    3    5    7    9    11   13   15   17   19   21
L    M    N    O    P    Q    R    S    T    U    V
23   25   27   29   31   33   35   37   39   41   43
W    X    Y    Z
45   47   49   51
```

1. 11 1   3   23 9   6. 11 41 27 27 49

   __ __ __ __ __   __ __ __ __ __

2. 31 15 49 37 17 5 1 23   7. 11 1   39 1   23

   __ __ __ __ __ __ __ __   __ __ __ __ __

3. 31 15 29 27 9   8. 11 9   39 5   15

   __ __ __ __ __   __ __ __ __ __

4. 11 29 41 27 7   9. 31 15 29 3   17 1

   __ __ __ __ __   __ __ __ __ __ __

5. 11 29 35 13 29 39   10. 11 17 9   35 5   9

   __ __ __ __ __ __   __ __ __ __ __ __

```
•WORD BOX•
FABLE          FETCH          FORGOT         FUNNY          PHONE
FATAL          FIERCE         FOUND          PHOBIA         PHYSICAL
```

SECRET CODES

/F/ MEDIAL POSITION

USE THE SECRET CODE TO SOLVE THE CODED WORDS. The answers are found at the bottom of this page in the Word Box.

_____ Say each word _____ times.
_____ Learn the definition of each word.
_____ Write a sentence for each word.
_____ Make up a story using some of the words from the puzzle.
_____ Draw pictures of some of the words from the puzzle.
_____ Play "I Spy." Look around the classroom and find the words or the objects they represent.

_____ _____ .

•SECRET CODE•

A	B	C	D	E	F	G	H	I	J	K
1	3	5	7	9	11	13	15	17	19	21
L	M	N	O	P	Q	R	S	T	U	V
23	25	27	29	31	33	35	37	39	41	43
W	X	Y	Z
45	47	49	51

1. 5 29 25 11 29 35 39

— — — — — — —

2. 7 9 11 17 27 9

— — — — — —

3. 3 41 11 11 9 39

— — — — — —

4. 9 11 11 9 5 39 17 43 9

— — — — — — — — —

5. 29 41 39 11 17 9 23 7

— — — — — — — —

6. 23 1 41 13 15 17 27 13

— — — — — — — —

7. 31 35 9 11 17 47

— — — — — —

8. 3 1 35 9 11 29 29 39

— — — — — — — —

9. 37 1 11 9 39 49

— — — — — —

10. 17 27 11 1 27 39

— — — — — —

•WORD BOX•

BAREFOOT	COMFORT	EFFECTIVE	LAUGHING	PREFIX
BUFFET	DEFINE	INFANT	OUTFIELD	SAFETY

SECRET CODES

/F/ FINAL POSITION

USE THE SECRET CODE TO SOLVE THE CODED WORDS. The answers are found at the bottom of this page in the Word Box.

_____ Say each word _____ times.
_____ Learn the definition of each word.
_____ Write a sentence for each word.
_____ Make up a story using some of the words from the puzzle.
_____ Draw pictures of some of the words from the puzzle.
_____ Play "I Spy." Look around the classroom and find the words or the objects they represent.

_____ _____ .

•SECRET CODE•

A	B	C	D	E	F	G	H	I	J	K
1	3	5	7	9	11	13	15	17	19	21
L	M	N	O	P	Q	R	S	T	U	V
23	25	27	29	31	33	35	37	39	41	43
W	X	Y	Z							
45	47	49	51							

1. 31 41 11 11

   — — — —

2. 9 27 29 41 13 15

   — — — — — —

3. 31 35 29 29 11

   — — — — —

4. 37 15 9 35 17 11 11

   — — — — — — —

5. 13 35 1 31 15

   — — — — —

6. 39 15 17 9 11

   — — — — —

7. 7 9 1 11

   — — — —

8. 5 15 17 9 11

   — — — — —

9. 3 9 23 17 9 11

   — — — — — —

10. 39 29 41 13 15

   — — — — —

•WORD BOX•

BELIEF	DEAF	GRAPH	PUFF	THIEF
CHIEF	ENOUGH	PROOF	SHERIFF	TOUGH

Name _____ Date _____

SCRAMBLED WORDS

/F/ INITIAL POSITION

UNSCRAMBLE THE WORDS. The answers are in the Word Box.

_____ Say each word _____ times.
_____ Learn the definition of each word.
_____ Write a sentence for each word.
_____ Make up a story using some of the words from the puzzle.
_____ Draw pictures of some of the words from the puzzle.
_____ Play "I Spy." Look around the classroom and find the words or the objects they represent.

_____ _____ .

1. INOFAHS   _____

2. SCTRFOEA   _____

3. OPHOT   _____

4. BLLTFOAO   _____

5. POOOOLFRF   _____

6. FSUS   _____

7. MFRA   _____

8. AFT   _____

9. THGIF   _____

10. FTRUEU   _____

11. NUF   _____

12. EOERVRF   _____

13. KROF   _____

14. LEDFI   _____

15. FRSTI   _____

•WORD BOX•				
FARM	FIELD	FOOLPROOF	FOREVER	FUSS
FASHION	FIGHT	FOOTBALL	FORK	FUTURE
FAT	FIRST	FORECAST	FUN	PHOTO

SCRAMBLED WORDS

/F/ MEDIAL POSITION

UNSCRAMBLE THE WORDS. The answers are in the Word Box.

_____ Say each word _____ times.
_____ Learn the definition of each word.
_____ Write a sentence for each word.
_____ Make up a story using some of the words from the puzzle.
_____ Draw pictures of some of the words from the puzzle.
_____ Play "I Spy." Look around the classroom and find the words or the objects they represent.

_____ _____ .

1. FEFECT   _____
2. FCAE   _____
3. FSUEUL   _____
4. ROTHPY   _____
5. TTOFUI   _____
6. TFRFAIC   _____
7. KBRFSTAEA   _____
8. GLFOER   _____
9. ENFECRO   _____
10. LEDHGIUFTL   _____
11. SOAF   _____
12. REFCIFO   _____
13. SFUFRE   _____
14. CLLOROUF   _____
15. FNCOUSE   _____

•WORD BOX•

BREAKFAST	CONFUSE	ENFORCE	OUTFIT	TRAFFIC
CAFE	DELIGHTFUL	GOLFER	SOFA	TROPHY
COLORFUL	EFFECT	OFFICER	SUFFER	USEFUL

SCRAMBLED WORDS

/F/ FINAL POSITION

UNSCRAMBLE THE WORDS. The answers are in the Word Box.

——— Say each word ——— times.
——— Learn the definition of each word.
——— Write a sentence for each word.
——— Make up a story using some of the words from the puzzle.
——— Draw pictures of some of the words from the puzzle.
——— Play "I Spy." Look around the classroom and find the words or the objects they represent.

——— ——————————————————————————————— .

1. RGPHATELE ———————————————
2. NEOUGH ———————————————
3. FNKEI ———————————————
4. EFARIGF ———————————————
5. FEHC ———————————————
6. GTHUO ———————————————
7. LBFEEI ———————————————
8. SHRFEIF ———————————————
9. FHCRKDNHAEIE ———————————————
10. PFRNRAIOO ———————————————
11. THFEI ———————————————
12. EFIL ———————————————
13. ROFO ———————————————
14. FEEB ———————————————
15. LGAHU ———————————————

•WORD BOX•				
BEEF	ENOUGH	KNIFE	RAINPROOF	TELEGRAPH
BELIEF	GIRAFFE	LAUGH	ROOF	THIEF
CHEF	HANDKERCHIEF	LIFE	SHERIFF	TOUGH

WORD FIND

/F/ INITIAL POSITION

FIND THE WORDS IN THE WORD BOX THAT ARE HIDDEN IN THE PUZZLE. They may be hidden down, across, upside down, diagonal, or backwards.

_____ Say each word _____ times.
_____ Learn the definition of each word.
_____ Write a sentence for each word.
_____ Make up a story using some of the words from the puzzle.
_____ Draw pictures of some of the words from the puzzle.
_____ Play "I Spy." Look around the classroom and find the words or the objects they represent.

_____ _____ .

```
M  W  B  Q  F  I  G  H  T  F  N  D  T  C
C  D  Y  U  D  N  K  F  M  P  F  C  T  X
F  I  S  H  A  J  N  B  T  D  R  U  C  A
X  V  P  O  F  S  F  A  L  L  Z  O  F  F
A  Y  E  R  I  F  L  F  R  T  E  H  N  I
F  F  V  Q  N  I  Z  E  F  O  Z  L  W  R
T  L  I  A  D  N  V  S  Y  F  U  H  J  E
E  T  F  B  V  E  K  R  E  C  A  F  L  M
G  F  B  Q  R  C  U  P  M  I  K  F  B  A
R  L  O  O  A  M  F  A  M  I  L  Y  C  N
O  J  F  H  T  G  L  P  F  O  F  Z  H  L
F  N  U  J  A  F  R  I  F  I  F  M  C  D
K  K  N  F  F  Y  L  N  E  Y  W  C  G  Z
M  C  F  U  N  E  R  A  L  J  V  A  D  T
T  A  Z  T  O  L  M  D  F  A  H  K  Q  F
```

• WORD BOX •

FACE	FILE	FIVE
FALL	FIND	FOREVER
FAMILY	FINE	FORGET
FAT	FIREMAN	FUN
FIGHT	FISH	FUNERAL

WORD FIND

/F/ MEDIAL POSITION

FIND THE WORDS IN THE WORD BOX THAT ARE HIDDEN IN THE PUZZLE. They may be hidden down, across, upside down, diagonal, or backwards.

_____ Say each word _____ times.
_____ Learn the definition of each word.
_____ Write a sentence for each word.
_____ Make up a story using some of the words from the puzzle.
_____ Draw pictures of some of the words from the puzzle.
_____ Play "I Spy." Look around the classroom and find the words or the objects they represent.

_____ _____ .

```
M  L  Y  O  F  S  T  I  F  L  E  Y  O  A  F
I  N  F  L  A  T  E  A  F  C  J  M  Y  C  V
F  U  N  F  A  I  R  E  D  F  E  U  B  D  L
T  P  X  L  F  Z  C  L  L  D  F  N  K  Y  Z
E  R  Z  R  M  P  T  E  R  R  I  F  I  C  F
R  E  N  Z  L  A  E  P  T  A  N  A  B  F  Y
E  F  B  C  P  F  V  H  V  F  U  S  X  M  L
F  S  T  D  F  R  Y  A  S  F  D  T  O  F  C
R  N  M  O  Q  F  A  N  Z  A  F  E  A  T  P
E  A  C  Q  I  W  M  T  Y  I  X  N  Z  N  T
T  R  S  R  L  E  L  M  T  R  O  F  T  E  N
N  T  R  S  G  O  L  D  F  I  S  H  N  P  A
I  E  T  V  O  R  M  I  N  F  A  N  T  X  B
T  C  O  U  T  F  I  T  L  T  O  F  V  C  D
```

•WORD BOX•

AFFAIR	INFLATE	TERRIFIC
COFFEE	INTERFERE	TERRIFY
ELEPHANT	OFTEN	TRANSFER
GOLDFISH	OUTFIT	UNFAIR
INFANT	STIFLE	UNFASTEN

WORD FIND

/F/ FINAL POSITION

FIND THE WORDS IN THE WORD BOX THAT ARE HIDDEN IN THE PUZZLE. They
may be hidden down, across, upside down, diagonal, or backwards.

_____ Say each word _____ times.
_____ Learn the definition of each word.
_____ Write a sentence for each word.
_____ Make up a story using some of the words from the puzzle.
_____ Draw pictures of some of the words from the puzzle.
_____ Play "I Spy." Look around the classroom and find the words or the objects they
represent.

_____ _____ .

```
F  C  X  F  A  C  O  U  G  H  T  F  Z  O  L  C
D  C  S  A  F  H  I  K  M  D  A  S  F  T  M  H
G  Y  A  X  A  L  O  O  F  J  N  C  O  Z  X  E
F  S  F  F  R  T  B  D  H  U  A  E  L  T  N  F
L  J  E  Y  Z  O  F  G  F  R  Q  N  A  P  L  Z
T  Z  H  F  F  X  U  F  Y  G  F  O  C  F  B  D
Z  E  X  O  C  A  C  G  O  H  N  U  K  E  L  A
Y  F  G  O  L  D  T  P  H  T  Y  G  A  I  M  C
C  I  F  R  P  Z  T  Z  C  X  R  H  F  L  L  D
L  N  Y  L  L  E  A  F  T  R  Z  F  M  E  F  Z
T  K  F  B  N  D  O  F  A  Y  E  K  T  B  L  O
R  Y  O  F  F  E  I  H  C  J  C  E  R  A  D  G
P  U  F  F  M  L  K  F  S  H  K  N  F  M  F  L
```

•WORD BOX•		
ALOOF	ENOUGH	REEF
BELIEF	KNIFE	ROOF
CHEF	LAUGH	ROUGH
CHIEF	LEAF	SAFE
COUGH	PUFF	SNUFF

Name _____   Date _____

CROSSWORD PUZZLE

/F/ INITIAL POSITION

COMPLETE THE PUZZLE. The answers are in the Word Box.

_____ Say each word _____ times.
_____ Learn the definition of each word.
_____ Write a sentence for each word.
_____ Make up a story using some of the words from the puzzle.
_____ Draw pictures of some of the words from the puzzle.
_____ Play "I Spy." Look around the classroom and find the words or the objects they represent.

_____ _____ .

```
•WORD BOX•

FABLE        FEATHERS      FEVER        FOREVER       PHOBIA
FATHER       FEED          FICTION      FOUR          PHONE
FAVORITE     FEUD          FIRE
```

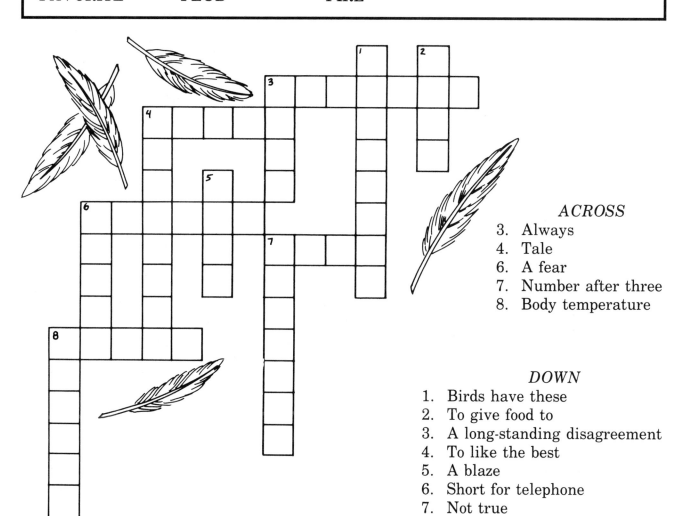

ACROSS
3. Always
4. Tale
6. A fear
7. Number after three
8. Body temperature

DOWN
1. Birds have these
2. To give food to
3. A long-standing disagreement
4. To like the best
5. A blaze
6. Short for telephone
7. Not true
8. Papa

CROSSWORD PUZZLE

/F/ MEDIAL POSITION

COMPLETE THE PUZZLE. The answers are in the Word Box.

_____ Say each word _____ times.
_____ Learn the definition of each word.
_____ Write a sentence for each word.
_____ Make up a story using some of the words from the puzzle.
_____ Draw pictures of some of the words from the puzzle.
_____ Play "I Spy." Look around the classroom and find the words or the objects they
represent.

_____ _____ .

•WORD BOX•

BAREFOOT	BUFFALO	SELFISH	SPITEFUL	THANKFUL
BEFORE	CAFETERIA	SOFA	SUFFER	THOROUGHFARE
BREAKFAST	DEFEND			

ACROSS
1. Furniture used for sitting
4. To protect
5. Western animal
7. Morning meal
8. Grateful
9. Malicious

DOWN
1. To endure hardships
2. Stingy
3. Passage
5. Previously
6. Lunchroom
7. Without shoes

CROSSWORD PUZZLE

/F/ FINAL POSITION

COMPLETE THE PUZZLE. The answers are in the Word Box.

_____ Say each word _____ times.
_____ Learn the definition of each word.
_____ Write a sentence for each word.
_____ Make up a story using some of the words from the puzzle.
_____ Draw pictures of some of the words from the puzzle.
_____ Play "I Spy." Look around the classroom and find the words or the objects they
represent.

_____ _____ .

•WORD BOX•				
GIRAFFE	IF	OFF	SHERIFF	TOUGH
GRAPH	LAUGH	ROOF	THIEF	WIFE
HUFF	LEAF	SAFE		

ACROSS
1. Grows on a tree
4. Design
5. Hard
8. Opposite of husband
9. Opposite of on
10. Maybe

DOWN
1. To make a happy sound
2. Protected
3. Law enforcement officer
4. Animal with a long neck
5. One who steals
6. To breathe heavily
7. Top of house

ACTIVITIES FOR /G/

WORD CIRCLES

/G/ INITIAL POSITION

FIND EVERY THIRD LETTER to find out what the puzzle says. Start at the arrow.

_____ Say each word _____ times.
_____ Learn the definition of each word.
_____ Write a sentence for each word.
_____ Make up a story using some of the words from the puzzle.
_____ Draw pictures of some of the words from the puzzle.
_____ Play "I Spy." Look around the classroom and find the words or the objects they represent.

_____ _____ .

Answer:_____

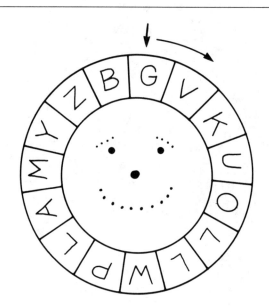

Answer:_____

Answer:_____

Answer:_____

Name _____ Date _____

WORD CIRCLES

/G/ MEDIAL POSITION

FIND EVERY THIRD LETTER to find out what the puzzle says. Start at the arrow.

_____ Say each word _____ times.
_____ Learn the definition of each word.
_____ Write a sentence for each word.
_____ Make up a story using some of the words from the puzzle.
_____ Draw pictures of some of the words from the puzzle.
_____ Play "I Spy." Look around the classroom and find the words or the objects they represent.

_____ _____ .

Answer: _____

Answer: _____

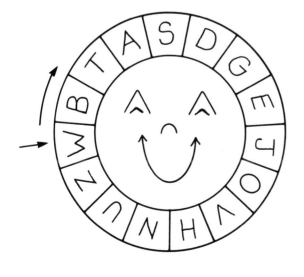

Answer: _____

Answer: _____

Name _____ Date _____

WORD CIRCLES

/G/ FINAL POSITION

FIND EVERY THIRD LETTER to find out what the puzzle says. Start at the arrow.

_____ Say each word _____ times.
_____ Learn the definition of each word.
_____ Write a sentence for each word.
_____ Make up a story using some of the words from the puzzle.
_____ Draw pictures of some of the words from the puzzle.
_____ Play "I Spy." Look around the classroom and find the words or the objects they
        represent.

_____ _____ .

Answer: _____   Answer: _____

Answer: _____   Answer: _____

Name _____   Date _____

DOTTED WORDS

/G/ INITIAL POSITION

COLOR THE DOTTED LETTERS to find the words.

_____ Say each word _____ times.
_____ Learn the definition of each word.
_____ Write a sentence for each word.
_____ Make up a story using one or both of the words from the puzzle.
_____ Draw pictures of one or both of the words from the puzzle.
_____ Play "I Spy." Look around the classroom and find the words or the objects they
         represent.

_____ .

ANSWERS: _____

Name _____ Date _____

DOTTED WORDS

/G/ MEDIAL POSITION

COLOR THE DOTTED LETTERS to find the words.

_____ Say each word _____ times.
_____ Learn the definition of each word.
_____ Write a sentence for each word.
_____ Make up a story using one or both of the words from the puzzle.
_____ Draw pictures of one or both of the words from the puzzle.
_____ Play "I Spy." Look around the classroom and find the words or the objects they represent.

_____ _____ .

ANSWERS: _____

Name _____   Date _____

DOTTED WORDS

/G/ FINAL POSITION

COLOR THE DOTTED LETTERS to find the words.

_____ Say each word _____ times.
_____ Learn the definition of each word.
_____ Write a sentence for each word.
_____ Make up a story using one or both of the words from the puzzle.
_____ Draw pictures of one or both of the words from the puzzle.
_____ Play "I Spy." Look around the classroom and find the words or the objects they represent.

_____ _____ .

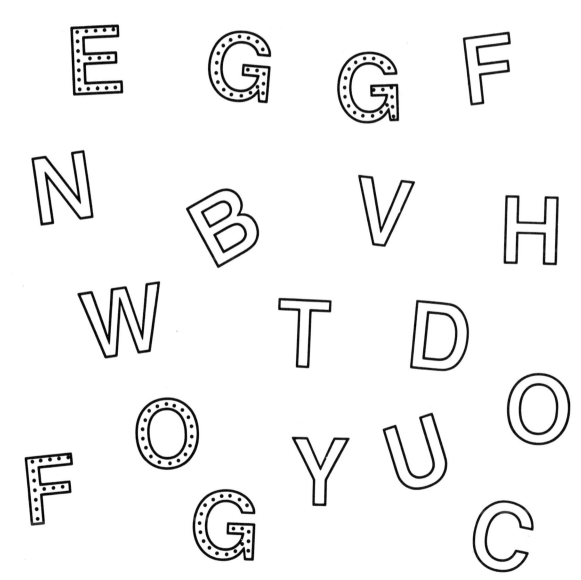

ANSWERS: _____   _____

Name _____   Date _____

SECRET CODES

/G/ INITIAL POSITION

USE THE SECRET CODE TO SOLVE THE CODED WORDS. The answers are found at the bottom of this page in the Word Box.

_____ Say each word _____ times.
_____ Learn the definition of each word.
_____ Write a sentence for each word.
_____ Make up a story using some of the words from the puzzle.
_____ Draw pictures of some of the words from the puzzle.
_____ Play "I Spy." Look around the classroom and find the words or the objects they represent.

_____ _____ .

•SECRET CODE•

A	B	C	D	E	F	G	H	I	J	K
2	4	6	8	10	12	14	16	18	20	22
L	M	N	O	P	Q	R	S	T	U	V
24	26	28	30	32	34	36	38	40	42	44
W	X	Y	Z							
46	48	50	52							

1. 14 2 24 10
   __ __ __ __

2. 14 42 10 38 38
   __ __ __ __ __

3. 14 2 52 10
   __ __ __ __

4. 14 42 18 24 40
   __ __ __ __ __

5. 14 42 38 40
   __ __ __ __

6. 14 30 24 8 10 28
   __ __ __ __ __ __

7. 14 42 26 8 36 30 32
   __ __ __ __ __ __ __

8. 14 30 36 50
   __ __ __ __

9. 14 10 50 38 10 36
   __ __ __ __ __ __

10. 14 30 4 24 10 40
    __ __ __ __ __ __

•WORD BOX•

GALE	GEYSER	GOLDEN	GUESS	GUMDROP
GAZE	GOBLET	GORY	GUILT	GUST

SECRET CODES

/G/ MEDIAL POSITION

USE THE SECRET CODE TO SOLVE THE CODED WORDS. The answers are found at the bottom of this page in the Word Box.

_____ Say each word _____ times.
_____ Learn the definition of each word.
_____ Write a sentence for each word.
_____ Make up a story using some of the words from the puzzle.
_____ Draw pictures of some of the words from the puzzle.
_____ Play "I Spy." Look around the classroom and find the words or the objects they represent.

_____ _____ .

•SECRET CODE•

A	B	C	D	E	F	G	H	I	J	K
2	4	6	8	10	12	14	16	18	20	22
L	M	N	O	P	Q	R	S	T	U	V
24	26	28	30	32	34	36	38	40	42	44
W	X	Y	Z							
46	48	50	52							

1. 2 24 24 18 14 2 40 30 36

— — — — — — — — —

2. 40 18 14 10 36

— — — — —

3. 6 30 42 14 2 36

— — — — — —

4. 8 18 38 14 42 38 40

— — — — — — —

5. 16 10 48 2 14 30 28

— — — — — — —

6. 2 14 30 28 50

— — — — —

7. 38 32 2 14 16 10 40 40 18

— — — — — — — — —

8. 44 18 28 10 14 2 36

— — — — — — —

9. 10 14 14 28 30 14

— — — — — —

10. 22 2 28 14 2 36 30 30

— — — — — — — —

•WORD BOX•

AGONY	COUGAR	EGGNOG	KANGAROO	TIGER
ALLIGATOR	DISGUST	HEXAGON	SPAGHETTI	VINEGAR

SECRET CODES

/G/   FINAL POSITION

USE THE SECRET CODE TO SOLVE THE CODED WORDS. The answers are found at the bottom of this page in the Word Box.

_____ Say each word _____ times.
_____ Learn the definition of each word.
_____ Write a sentence for each word.
_____ Make up a story using some of the words from the puzzle.
_____ Draw pictures of some of the words from the puzzle.
_____ Play "I Spy." Look around the classroom and find the words or the objects they represent.

_____ _____ .

•SECRET CODE•										
A	**B**	**C**	**D**	**E**	**F**	**G**	**H**	**I**	**J**	**K**
2	4	6	8	10	12	14	16	18	20	22
L	**M**	**N**	**O**	**P**	**Q**	**R**	**S**	**T**	**U**	**V**
24	26	28	30	32	34	36	38	40	42	44
W	**X**	**Y**	**Z**							
46	48	50	62							

1. 14   2   28   14
    __ __ __ __

2. 4   42   14
    __ __ __

3. 12   36   30   14
    __ __ __ __

4. 12   2   40   18   14   42   10
    __ __ __ __ __ __ __

5. 6   2   40   2   24   30   14
    __ __ __ __ __ __ __

6. 32   30   24   24   18   46   30   14
    __ __ __ __ __ __ __ __

7. 16   30   40   8   30   14
    __ __ __   __ __ __

8. 46   2   38   16   36   2   14
    __ __ __ __ __ __ __

9. 36   42   14
    __ __ __

10. 52   18   14   52   2   14
    __ __ __ __ __ __

•WORD BOX•				
BUG	FATIGUE	GANG	POLLIWOG	WASHRAG
CATALOG	FROG	HOT DOG	RUG	ZIGZAG

Name _____   Date _____

SCRAMBLED WORDS

/G/ INITIAL POSITION

UNSCRAMBLE THE WORDS. The answers are in the Word Box.

_____ Say each word _____ times.
_____ Learn the definition of each word.
_____ Write a sentence for each word.
_____ Make up a story using some of the words from the puzzle.
_____ Draw pictures of some of the words from the puzzle.
_____ Play "I Spy." Look around the classroom and find the words or the objects they
        represent.

_____ _____ .

1. ATEG   _____

2. ZGAE   _____

3. FGOL   _____

4. LFUG   _____

5. GEANSOIL   _____

6. GTLIU   _____

7. DRUAG   _____

8. YGTEAWA   _____

9. GGROOUES   _____

10. ABG   _____

11. TGRHI   _____

12. TGRHAE   _____

13. SREYGE   _____

14. SHOTG   _____

15. AEVLG   _____

•WORD BOX•				
GAB	GATHER	GETAWAY	GIRTH	GUARD
GASOLINE	GAVEL	GEYSER	GOLF	GUILT
GATE	GAZE	GHOST	GORGEOUS	GULF

SCRAMBLED WORDS

/G/ MEDIAL POSITION

UNSCRAMBLE THE WORDS. The answers are in the Word Box.

_____ Say each word _____ times.
_____ Learn the definition of each word.
_____ Write a sentence for each word.
_____ Make up a story using some of the words from the puzzle.
_____ Draw pictures of some of the words from the puzzle.
_____ Play "I Spy." Look around the classroom and find the words or the objects they represent.

_____ _____ .

1. OAURGC   _____

2. BGRGIE   _____

3. RGNFIE   _____

4. DAOGRN   _____

5. AAGNI   _____

6. TRGEI   _____

7. TRGEOHET   _____

8. AOGYN   _____

9. PGSAHTETI   _____

10. AGREN   _____

11. GSUTSDI   _____

12. GSUEISDI   _____

13. GONWA   _____

14. GNEIATVE   _____

15. RLRAGUE   _____

•WORD BOX•

AGAIN	BIGGER	DISGUST	NEGATIVE	TIGER
AGONY	COUGAR	DRAGON	REGULAR	TOGETHER
ANGER	DISGUISE	FINGER	SPAGHETTI	WAGON

Name _____   Date _____

SCRAMBLED WORDS

/G/ FINAL POSITION

UNSCRAMBLE THE WORDS. The answers are in the Word Box.

_____ Say each word _____ times.
_____ Learn the definition of each word.
_____ Write a sentence for each word.
_____ Make up a story using some of the words from the puzzle.
_____ Draw pictures of some of the words from the puzzle.
_____ Play "I Spy." Look around the classroom and find the words or the objects they
represent.

_____ _____ .

1. TGA   _____

2. BGA   _____

3. RGA   _____

4. GWIT   _____

5. GFOR   _____

6. OOGDHT   _____

7. TGIAFUE   _____

8. BGU   _____

9. AACOTLG   _____

10. UGH   _____

11. GLEEUA   _____

12. EVGUA   _____

13. GOLC   _____

14. LODGAIEU   _____

15. NETGUM   _____

•WORD BOX•				
BAG	CLOG	FROG	LEAGUE	TAG
BUG	DIALOGUE	HOT DOG	NUTMEG	TWIG
CATALOG	FATIGUE	HUG	RAG	VAGUE

WORD FIND

/G/ INITIAL POSITION

FIND THE WORDS IN THE WORD BOX THAT ARE HIDDEN IN THE PUZZLE. They
may be hidden down, across, upside down, diagonal, or backwards.

_____ Say each word _____ times.
_____ Learn the definition of each word.
_____ Write a sentence for each word.
_____ Make up a story using some of the words from the puzzle.
_____ Draw pictures of some of the words from the puzzle.
_____ Play "I Spy." Look around the classroom and find the words or the objects they
        represent.

_____ _____ .

```
D  G  L  M  G  U  R  G  L  E  I  N  F  A
H  C  Q  N  E  V  I  G  P  G  W  H  G  O
L  G  T  D  G  S  K  E  J  B  S  F  Y  B
H  I  G  E  T  T  I  N  G  I  U  U  X  S
G  K  J  A  K  E  D  B  F  C  G  V  B  E
A  T  G  I  R  L  R  D  G  E  E  S  E  L
S  M  A  J  L  T  L  G  Z  A  S  T  Y  G
A  K  J  G  N  O  H  O  G  U  E  S  T  G
G  D  L  O  G  L  E  R  T  G  S  J  K  O
D  A  R  I  C  O  L  Y  N  O  B  M  U  G
T  T  L  N  B  K  A  L  T  L  G  G  L  D
L  B  G  G  G  F  T  A  O  G  G  G  G  G
```

•WORD BOX•

GAS	GOAT	GORY
GEESE	GOGGLES	GUEST
GETTING	GOING	GUMBO
GIRL	GOLD	GURGLE
GIVEN	GOLDFISH	GUY

Name _____   Date _____

WORD FIND

/G/ MEDIAL POSITION

FIND THE WORDS IN THE WORD BOX THAT ARE HIDDEN IN THE PUZZLE. They
may be hidden down, across, upside down, diagonal, or backwards.

_____ Say each word _____ times.
_____ Learn the definition of each word.
_____ Write a sentence for each word.
_____ Make up a story using some of the words from the puzzle.
_____ Draw pictures of some of the words from the puzzle.
_____ Play "I Spy." Look around the classroom and find the words or the objects they
represent.

_____ _____ .

```
L  I  A  D  F  Q  Z  B  E  K  F  I  L  Y  M  R  B
D  T  U  E  I  L  K  J  I  Z  M  E  G  O  W  E  G
N  T  H  M  C  A  F  D  L  G  F  A  J  G  R  U  S
E  E  R  Y  L  J  I  S  H  T  D  Q  S  A  G  A  G
G  H  G  F  D  S  N  P  N  I  P  A  N  D  P  T  V
A  G  Y  G  G  O  G  N  X  E  G  S  H  E  L  L
T  A  V  U  C  G  M  E  T  H  O  V  A  R  V  F  C  K
I  P  I  K  G  X  R  U  A  G  S  I  Z  Y  Q  R  M
V  S  Z  Q  R  N  G  O  G  A  X  N  B  K  A  S  E
E  K  X  V  A  T  M  G  A  T  P  S  A  G  W  A  O
T  I  C  Z  G  B  W  X  I  Y  J  T  U  B  G  C  A
G  W  L  G  G  G  H  N  D  G  O  K  E  F  T  D
B  I  G  G  E  S  T  O  U  G  C  V  R  A  Y  C  E
M  G  A  Z  B  A  G  G  A  G  E  K  S  G  B  S  G
```

+---+
| •WORD BOX• |
| AGAIN   COUGAR   FINGER |
| AGAINST   DISGUISE   NEGATIVE |
| BAGGAGE   EAGER   SAGA |
| BEGGAR   EGGSHELL   SPAGHETTI |
| BIGGEST   EGO   YOGA |
+---+

WORD FIND

/G/ FINAL POSITION

FIND THE WORDS IN THE WORD BOX THAT ARE HIDDEN IN THE PUZZLE. They may be hidden down, across, upside down, diagonal, or backwards.

_____ Say each word _____ times.
_____ Learn the definition of each word.
_____ Write a sentence for each word.
_____ Make up a story using some of the words from the puzzle.
_____ Draw pictures of some of the words from the puzzle.
_____ Play "I Spy." Look around the classroom and find the words or the objects they represent.

_____ _____ .

```
J  U  Q  H  F  A  T  I  G  U  E  G  P  B
R  R  V  S  M  G  Y  L  O  G  F  D  N  Z
E  I  O  V  F  I  G  N  C  X  K  H  G  E
N  J  G  E  M  K  G  H  O  W  A  M  Y  U
E  R  U  N  G  O  G  U  Z  N  O  F  G  G
G  L  E  U  D  C  Y  G  D  T  V  A  A  I
E  Q  D  T  B  L  T  B  B  A  G  E  T  R
W  K  O  M  F  C  A  T  A  L  O  G  S  T
P  H  X  E  S  G  H  C  B  U  G  D  X  N
T  L  I  G  A  G  T  F  L  A  G  U  B  I
```

• WORD BOX •

BAG	FLAG	LOG
BUG	HANDBAG	NUTMEG
CATALOG	HOT DOG	RENEGE
FATIGUE	HUG	STAG
FIG	INTRIGUE	VOGUE

CROSSWORD PUZZLE

/G/ INITIAL POSITION

COMPLETE THE PUZZLE. The answers are in the Word Box.

_____ Say each word _____ times.
_____ Learn the definition of each word.
_____ Write a sentence for each word.
_____ Make up a story using some of the words from the puzzle.
_____ Draw pictures of some of the words from the puzzle.
_____ Play "I Spy." Look around the classroom and find the words or the objects they
represent.

_____ _____ .

```
•WORD BOX•
GALLON      GARDENIA    GIVE      GOOD       GOSSIP
GAMBLE      GASOLINE    GOAT      GOODBYE    GOVERNMENT
GAME        GEESE       GOING     GORILLA    GUEST
GARDENER
```

ACROSS
1. One who tends a garden
3. Something you like
4. Flower
5. To bet
6. To talk about
8. Honking animals
9. Leaving
11. To bestow

DOWN
1. A body of authority
2. An animal that will eat almost
   anything
3. Fuel for cars
4. Large ape
5. Farewell
6. Amount of liquid
7. A person who comes for a visit
10. Something you play

Name _____   Date _____

CROSSWORD PUZZLE

/G/ MEDIAL POSITION

COMPLETE THE PUZZLE. The answers are in the Word Box.

_____ Say each word _____ times.
_____ Learn the definition of each word.
_____ Write a sentence for each word.
_____ Make up a story using some of the words from the puzzle.
_____ Draw pictures of some of the words from the puzzle.
_____ Play "I Spy." Look around the classroom and find the words or the objects they represent.

_____ _____ .

•WORD BOX•

ALLIGATOR	EAGER	LUGGAGE	MEAGER	SPAGHETTI
CIGAR	FINGER	MAGAZINES	SAGA	TIGER
COUGAR	LEGAL	MAGNIFICENT		

ACROSS

2. Story
5. Long noodles
7. Law
8. Part of a hand
10. Anxious
11. Big cigarette
12. Wildcat

DOWN

1. Periodicals
3. Wildcat with stripes
4. Marvelous
6. An animal resembling a crocodile
7. Baggage
9. Slim

Name _____ Date _____

CROSSWORD PUZZLE

/G/ FINAL POSITION

COMPLETE THE PUZZLE. The answers are in the Word Box.

_____ Say each word _____ times.
_____ Learn the definition of each word.
_____ Write a sentence for each word.
_____ Make up a story using some of the words from the puzzle.
_____ Draw pictures of some of the words from the puzzle.
_____ Play "I Spy." Look around the classroom and find the words or the objects they represent.

_____ _____ .

•WORD BOX•				
BAG	DIALOGUE	FATIGUE	ICEBAG	WASHRAG
BRAG	DIG	FOG	LEG	WIG
CATALOG	DOG	FROG	TUG	

ACROSS
2. To tire
4. Book used for ordering
7. Canine
9. Cloth used for cleaning
10. Green animal
12. Coldpack

DOWN
1. Sack
2. Low clouds
3. To pull
5. Limb
6. Conversation
7. To remove dirt with a shovel
8. To boast
11. Hairpiece

ACTIVITIES FOR / J /

WORD CIRCLES

/J/ INITIAL POSITION

FIND EVERY THIRD LETTER to find out what the puzzle says. Start at the arrow.

_____ Say each word _____ times.
_____ Learn the definition of each word.
_____ Write a sentence for each word.
_____ Make up a story using some of the words from the puzzle.
_____ Draw pictures of some of the words from the puzzle.
_____ Play "I Spy." Look around the classroom and find the words or the objects they represent.

_____ .

Answer:_____   Answer:_____

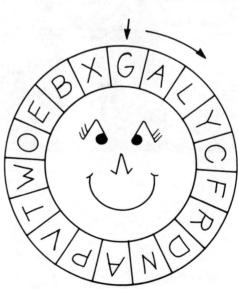

Answer: _____   Answer: _____

WORD CIRCLES

/J/ MEDIAL POSITION

FIND EVERY THIRD LETTER to find out what the puzzle says. Start at the arrow.

_____ Say each word _____ times.
_____ Learn the definition of each word.
_____ Write a sentence for each word.
_____ Make up a story using some of the words from the puzzle.
_____ Draw pictures of some of the words from the puzzle.
_____ Play "I Spy." Look around the classroom and find the words or the objects they represent.

_____ _____ .

Answer: _____

Answer: _____

Answer: _____

Answer: _____

Name _____   Date _____

WORD CIRCLES

/J/ FINAL POSITION

FIND EVERY THIRD LETTER to find out what the puzzle says. Start at the arrow.

_____ Say each word _____ times.
_____ Learn the definition of each word.
_____ Write a sentence for each word.
_____ Make up a story using some of the words from the puzzle.
_____ Draw pictures of some of the words from the puzzle.
_____ Play "I Spy." Look around the classroom and find the words or the objects they
represent.

_____ _____ .

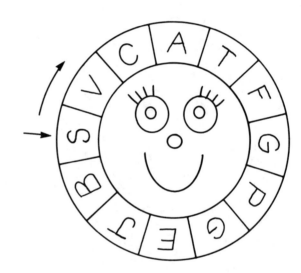

Answer: _____   Answer: _____

Answer: _____   Answer: _____

Name _____ Date _____

DOTTED WORDS

/J/ INITIAL POSITION

COLOR THE DOTTED LETTERS to find the words.

_____ Say each word _____ times.
_____ Learn the definition of each word.
_____ Write a sentence for each word.
_____ Make up a story using one or both of the words from the puzzle.
_____ Draw pictures of one or both of the words from the puzzle.
_____ Play "I Spy." Look around the classroom and find the words or the objects they
        represent.

_____ _____ .

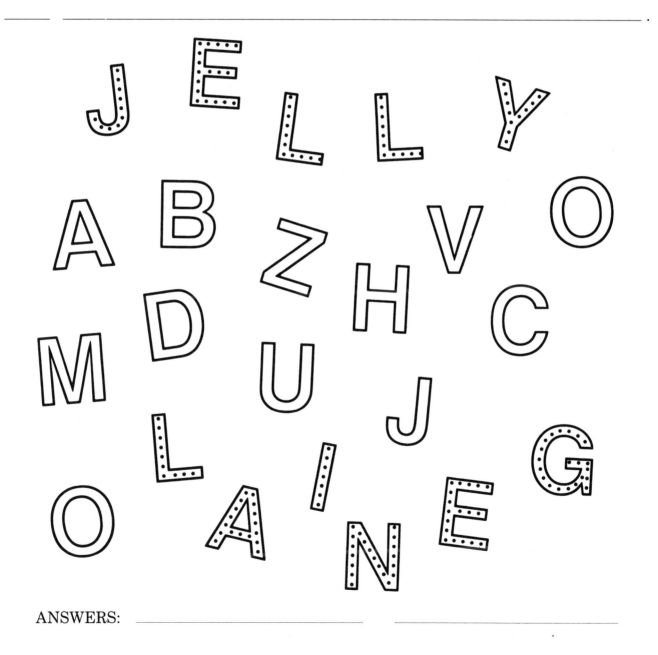

ANSWERS: _____ _____

Name _____ Date _____

DOTTED WORDS

/J/ MEDIAL POSITION

COLOR THE DOTTED LETTERS to find the words.

_____ Say each word _____ times.
_____ Learn the definition of each word.
_____ Write a sentence for each word.
_____ Make up a story using one or both of the words from the puzzle.
_____ Draw pictures of one or both of the words from the puzzle.
_____ Play "I Spy." Look around the classroom and find the words or the objects they represent.

_____ _____ .

ANSWERS: _____   _____

DOTTED WORDS

/J/ FINAL POSITION

COLOR THE DOTTED LETTERS to find the words.

_____ Say each word _____ times.
_____ Learn the definition of each word.
_____ Write a sentence for each word.
_____ Make up a story using one or both of the words from the puzzle.
_____ Draw pictures of one or both of the words from the puzzle.
_____ Play "I Spy." Look around the classroom and find the words or the objects they represent.

_____ .

ANSWERS: _____   _____

Name _____ Date _____

SECRET CODES

/J/ INITIAL POSITION

USE THE SECRET CODE TO SOLVE THE CODED WORDS. The answers are found at the bottom of this page in the Word Box.

_____ Say each word _____ times.
_____ Learn the definition of each word.
_____ Write a sentence for each word.
_____ Make up a story using some of the words from the puzzle.
_____ Draw pictures of some of the words from the puzzle.
_____ Play "I Spy." Look around the classroom and find the words or the objects they represent.

_____ _____ .

		•SECRET CODE•								
A	B	C	D	E	F	G	H	I	J	K
1	2	3	4	5	6	7	8	9	10	11
L	M	N	O	P	Q	R	S	T	U	V
12	13	14	15	16	17	18	19	20	21	22
W	X	Y	Z							
23	24	25	26							

1. 10 21 18 25

   __ __ __ __

2. 10 5 20

   __ __ __

3. 7 25 13

   __ __ __

4. 10 1 23

   __ __ __

5. 10 5 18 11 5 4

   __ __ __ __ __ __

6. 7 9 1 14 20

   __ __ __ __ __

7. 10 21 9 3 5

   __ __ __ __ __

8. 10 1 3 11 5 20

   __ __ __ __ __ __

9. 10 5 12 12 25

   __ __ __ __ __

10. 10 15 12 12 25

   __ __ __ __ __

•WORD BOX•				
GIANT	JACKET	JELLY	JET	JUICE
GYM	JAW	JERKED	JOLLY	JURY

SECRET CODES

/J/ MEDIAL POSITION

USE THE SECRET CODE TO SOLVE THE CODED WORDS. The answers are found at the bottom of this page in the Word Box.

_____ Say each word _____ times.
_____ Learn the definition of each word.
_____ Write a sentence for each word.
_____ Make up a story using some of the words from the puzzle.
_____ Draw pictures of some of the words from the puzzle.
_____ Play "I Spy." Look around the classroom and find the words or the objects they represent.

_____ _____ .

•SECRET CODE•

A	B	C	D	E	F	G	H	I	J	K
1	2	3	4	5	6	7	8	9	10	11
L	M	N	O	P	Q	R	S	T	U	V
12	13	14	15	16	17	18	19	20	21	22
W	X	Y	Z							
23	24	25	26							

1. 2 21 4 7 5 20
— — — — — —

2. 14 9 20 18 15 7 5 14
— — — — — — — —

3. 4 9 7 5 19 20
— — — — — —

4. 23 1 7 5 19
— — — — —

5. 18 5 10 5 3 20
— — — — — —

6. 1 4 10 21 19 20
— — — — — —

7. 20 18 1 7 9 3
— — — — — —

8. 3 1 7 5 19
— — — — —

9. 15 2 10 5 3 20 5 4
— — — — — — — —

10. 1 7 5 14 20
— — — — —

•WORD BOX•

ADJUST	BUDGET	DIGEST	OBJECTED	TRAGIC
AGENT	CAGES	NITROGEN	REJECT	WAGES

Name _____   Date _____

SECRET CODES

/J/ FINAL POSITION

USE THE SECRET CODE TO SOLVE THE CODED WORDS. The answers are found at the bottom of this page in the Word Box.

_____ Say each word _____ times.
_____ Learn the definition of each word.
_____ Write a sentence for each word.
_____ Make up a story using some of the words from the puzzle.
_____ Draw pictures of some of the words from the puzzle.
_____ Play "I Spy." Look around the classroom and find the words or the objects they represent.

_____ _____ .

•SECRET CODE•

A	B	C	D	E	F	G	H	I	J	K
1	2	3	4	5	6	7	8	9	10	11
L	M	N	O	P	Q	R	S	T	U	V
12	13	14	15	16	17	18	19	20	21	22
W	X	Y	Z							
23	24	25	26							

---

1. 4 15 4 7 5

    — — — — —

2. 13 5 19 19 1 7 5

    — — — — — — —

3. 22 15 25 1 7 5

    — — — — — —

4. 12 1 14 7 21 1 7 5

    — — — — — — — —

5. 1 2 18 9 4 7 5

    — — — — — — —

6. 4 15 19 1 7 5

    — — — — — —

7. 19 20 1 7 5

    — — — — —

8. 16 15 18 18 9 4 7 5

    — — — — — — — —

9. 6 21 4 7 5

    — — — — —

10. 15 22 5 18 1 7 5

    — — — — — — —

•WORD BOX•

ABRIDGE	DOSAGE	LANGUAGE	OVERAGE	STAGE
DODGE	FUDGE	MESSAGE	PORRIDGE	VOYAGE

Name _____   Date _____

SCRAMBLED WORDS

/J/ INITIAL POSITION

UNSCRAMBLE THE WORDS. The answers are in the Word Box.

_____ Say each word _____ times.
_____ Learn the definition of each word.
_____ Write a sentence for each word.
_____ Make up a story using some of the words from the puzzle.
_____ Draw pictures of some of the words from the puzzle.
_____ Play "I Spy." Look around the classroom and find the words or the objects they
       represent.

_____ _____ .

1. JSUTCIE   _____

2. JLOLY   _____

3. GNEES   _____

4. ROTJANI   _____

5. GTINA   _____

6. GINESU   _____

7. YLLEJ   _____

8. GNEREAL   _____

9. JEWLE   _____

10. JNURIO   _____

11. PUTREJI   _____

12. JELGNU   _____

13. EEUINNG   _____

14. OGOGELY   _____

15. ONJLRUA   _____

•WORD BOX•

GENERAL	GENUINE	JANITOR	JOLLY	JUNIOR
GENES	GEOLOGY	JELLY	JOURNAL	JUPITER
GENIUS	GIANT	JEWEL	JUNGLE	JUSTICE

Name _____ Date _____

SCRAMBLED WORDS

/J/ MEDIAL POSITION

UNSCRAMBLE THE WORDS. The answers are in the Word Box.

_____ Say each word _____ times.
_____ Learn the definition of each word.
_____ Write a sentence for each word.
_____ Make up a story using some of the words from the puzzle.
_____ Draw pictures of some of the words from the puzzle.
_____ Play "I Spy." Look around the classroom and find the words or the objects they represent.

_____ _____ .

1. NXYGOE _____

2. GCYNAE _____

3. JREOCIE _____

4. GAWSE _____

5. TRAYDEG _____

6. DESTIG _____

7. BOJECT _____

8. TLTLNINIGEE _____

9. NAGERTEE _____

10. FRIREGRAEROT _____

11. JAAR _____

12. ROMAJ _____

13. TASJMEY _____

14. NEILIROG _____

15. LIYBOOG _____

•WORD BOX•

AGENCY	DIGEST	MAJOR	REFRIGERATOR	TEENAGER
AJAR	INTELLIGENT	OBJECT	REJOICE	TRAGEDY
BIOLOGY	MAJESTY	OXYGEN	RELIGION	WAGES

Name _____ Date _____

SCRAMBLED WORDS

/J/ FINAL POSITION

UNSCRAMBLE THE WORDS. The answers are in the Word Box.

_____ Say each word _____ times.
_____ Learn the definition of each word.
_____ Write a sentence for each word.
_____ Make up a story using some of the words from the puzzle.
_____ Draw pictures of some of the words from the puzzle.
_____ Play "I Spy." Look around the classroom and find the words or the objects they
       represent.

_____ _____ .

1. EGAC   _____

2. EGAP   _____

3. EGABRAG   _____

4. EGADAM   _____

5. EGAIMRAR   _____

6. GLUGEAG   _____

7. EGANRTS   _____

8. AGAVEER   _____

9. PAGKCAE   _____

10. EGASOTR   _____

11. LVGASEA   _____

12. YGEAVO   _____

13. LIVGEAL   _____

14. EEEVBRGA   _____

15. ADNATVGEA   _____

+---+
| •WORD BOX• |
| ADVANTAGE   CAGE   LUGGAGE   PAGE   STRANGE |
| AVERAGE   DAMAGE   MARRIAGE   SALVAGE   VILLAGE |
| BEVERAGE   GARBAGE   PACKAGE   STORAGE   VOYAGE |
+---+

WORD FIND

/J/ INITIAL POSITION

FIND THE WORDS IN THE WORD BOX THAT ARE HIDDEN IN THE PUZZLE. They may be hidden down, across, upside down, diagonal, or backwards.

_____ Say each word _____ times.
_____ Learn the definition of each word.
_____ Write a sentence for each word.
_____ Make up a story using some of the words from the puzzle.
_____ Draw pictures of some of the words from the puzzle.
_____ Play "I Spy." Look around the classroom and find the words or the objects they represent.

_____ _____ .

```
T  R  Z  M  L  P  T  A  B  J  E  S  T  E  R
O  V  G  I  B  L  E  T  Y  A  Z  T  J  A  J
A  D  C  B  I  F  J  Y  L  L  O  J  K  S  U
Q  X  R  J  Y  G  K  E  X  O  W  D  N  V  H
G  I  G  A  N  T  I  C  L  P  M  J  O  T  A
P  F  Z  A  Q  N  O  M  C  Y  U  L  T  W  F
J  P  D  J  E  T  T  Y  L  A  K  C  A  J  Q
U  Q  N  G  E  N  T  L  E  M  A  N  I  A  P
D  B  S  V  Y  M  B  J  S  N  V  T  X  R  M
G  Z  Y  J  R  G  E  N  E  S  P  X  L  R  Q
E  C  J  J  T  O  O  U  J  W  R  T  M  E  K
D  M  Z  J  U  R  Y  J  U  M  B  O  J  D  N
```

•WORD BOX•		
GENES	JALOPY	JOLLY
GENTLEMAN	JARRED	JOT
GIBLET	JESTER	JUDGE
GIGANTIC	JETTY	JUMBO
JACKAL	JILT	JURY

WORD FIND

/J/ MEDIAL POSITION

FIND THE WORDS IN THE WORD BOX THAT ARE HIDDEN IN THE PUZZLE. They may be hidden down, across, upside down, diagonal, or backwards.

_____ Say each word _____ times.
_____ Learn the definition of each word.
_____ Write a sentence for each word.
_____ Make up a story using some of the words from the puzzle.
_____ Draw pictures of some of the words from the puzzle.
_____ Play "I Spy." Look around the classroom and find the words or the objects they
          represent.

_____ _____ .

```
J  A  E  I  N  O  I  G  E  R  J  M  J
B  J  J  C  A  B  B  A  G  E  S  T  L
D  C  A  G  E  L  E  S  S  K  B  R  E
F  O  J  O  K  U  C  R  G  C  I  E  T
N  G  P  T  Q  L  E  X  U  Y  O  F  I
I  I  B  O  W  G  D  D  T  A  L  U  O
G  T  D  L  D  Z  G  S  C  T  O  G  L
I  A  H  O  R  E  E  U  E  G  G  E  O
R  T  C  G  L  B  S  E  J  D  Y  E  G
O  E  F  Y  B  U  D  G  E  T  J  H  Y
J  C  V  E  D  U  C  A  T  O  R  Y  J
```

•WORD BOX•		
AGELESS	COGITATE	ETIOLOGY
BIOLOGY	CUDGEL	ORIGIN
BUDGET	EDGES	OTOLOGY
CABBAGES	EDUCATOR	REFUGEE
CODGER	EJECT	REGION

Name _____   Date _____

WORD FIND

/J/ FINAL POSITION

FIND THE WORDS IN THE WORD BOX THAT ARE HIDDEN IN THE PUZZLE. They
may be hidden down, across, upside down, diagonal, or backwards.

_____ Say each word _____ times.
_____ Learn the definition of each word.
_____ Write a sentence for each word.
_____ Make up a story using some of the words from the puzzle.
_____ Draw pictures of some of the words from the puzzle.
_____ Play "I Spy." Look around the classroom and find the words or the objects they
represent.

_____   _____ .

```
Q  P  R  U  Q  T  U  P  Y  B  T  M  A  J  D
F  G  B  A  N  D  A  G  E  Z  N  I  V  P  L
K  C  M  R  F  V  O  G  E  H  U  G  E  C  U
E  G  D  E  L  R  A  G  J  D  J  R  N  L  K
G  A  S  G  M  R  A  X  N  S  C  T  G  J  S
A  W  Q  B  U  R  V  C  H  E  Y  K  E  B  A
T  C  J  O  E  J  E  L  N  S  M  U  D  G  E
I  H  C  V  I  D  R  T  E  I  M  A  G  E  R
R  N  E  N  G  J  A  E  M  K  L  O  D  G  E
E  B  T  A  P  G  G  K  O  B  L  I  G  E  Z
H  E  D  G  E  L  E  G  D  U  F  P  D  Q  F
```

┌───┐
| •WORD BOX• |
| AVENGE   FUDGE   LEDGE |
| AVERAGE   HEDGE   LODGE |
| BANDAGE   HERITAGE   OBLIGE |
| BEVERAGE   HUGE   PERCENTAGE |
| ENCOURAGE   IMAGE   SMUDGE |
└───┘

Name _____   Date _____

CROSSWORD PUZZLE

/J/ INITIAL POSITION

COMPLETE THE PUZZLE. The answers are in the Word Box.

_____ Say each word _____ times.
_____ Learn the definition of each word.
_____ Write a sentence for each word.
_____ Make up a story using some of the words from the puzzle.
_____ Draw pictures of some of the words from the puzzle.
_____ Play "I Spy." Look around the classroom and find the words or the objects they represent.

_____ _____ .

•WORD BOX•				
GENUINE	JELLY	JOLT	JUICE	JUNIOR
GYM	JEWEL	JOURNEY	JUMBO	JUVENILE
JAR	JOKE	JOYFUL	JUNCTION	

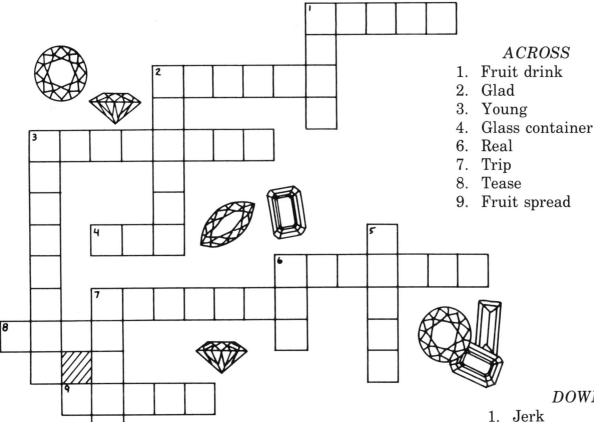

ACROSS
1. Fruit drink
2. Glad
3. Young
4. Glass container
6. Real
7. Trip
8. Tease
9. Fruit spread

DOWN
1. Jerk
2. Younger
3. Joining
5. Large
6. Sports auditorium
7. Gem

CROSSWORD PUZZLE

/J/ MEDIAL POSITION

COMPLETE THE PUZZLE. The answers are in the Word Box.

_____ Say each word _____ times.
_____ Learn the definition of each word.
_____ Write a sentence for each word.
_____ Make up a story using some of the words from the puzzle.
_____ Draw pictures of some of the words from the puzzle.
_____ Play "I Spy." Look around the classroom and find the words or the objects they
represent.

_____ _____ .

•WORD BOX•

EJECT	GADGET	OBJECT	RIGID	TRAGIC
FRIGID	LEGEND	OXYGEN	SOLDIER	WAGES

ACROSS
1. Air
2. To kick out
5. A thingamajig
6. Military person
9. Cold

DOWN
1. A thing
3. Disastrous
4. Pay
7. Story
8. Stiff

Name _____ Date _____

CROSSWORD PUZZLE

/J/ FINAL POSITION

COMPLETE THE PUZZLE. The answers are in the Word Box.

_____ Sav each word _____ times.
_____ Learn the definition of each word.
_____ Write a sentence for each word.
_____ Make up a story using some of the words from the puzzle.
_____ Draw pictures of some of the words from the puzzle.
_____ Play "I Spy." Look around the classroom and find the words or the objects they represent.

_____ _____ .

```
┌──────────────────────────────────────────────────────────────────┐
│                          •WORD BOX•                                │
│   BRIDGE        EDGE          LUGGAGE        PAGE        VILLAGE    │
│   CAGE          GARBAGE       MESSAGE        RAGE        VOYAGE     │
│   DAMAGE                                                            │
└──────────────────────────────────────────────────────────────────┘
```

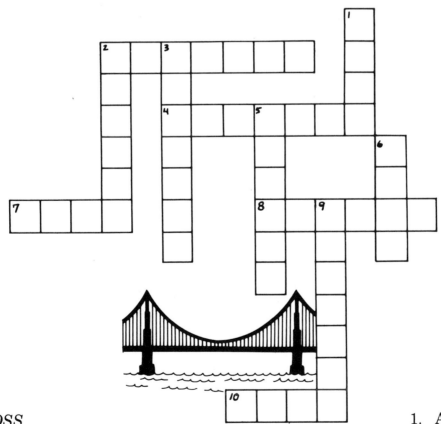

ACROSS	DOWN
2. Town	1. A sheet of paper
4. Trash	2. Trip
7. Border	3. Suitcases
8. To break	5. A road over water
10. To trap	6. Anger
	9. Note

ACTIVITIES FOR /K/

Name _____   Date _____

WORD CIRCLES

/K/ INITIAL POSITION

FIND EVERY THIRD LETTER to find out what the puzzle says. Start at the arrow.

_____ Say each word _____ times.
_____ Learn the definition of each word.
_____ Write a sentence for each word.
_____ Make up a story using some of the words from the puzzle.
_____ Draw pictures of some of the words from the puzzle.
_____ Play "I Spy." Look around the classroom and find the words or the objects they represent.

_____ _____ .

Answer: _____

Answer: _____

Answer: _____

Answer: _____

WORD CIRCLES

/K/ MEDIAL POSITION

FIND EVERY THIRD LETTER to find out what the puzzle says. Start at the arrow.

_____ Say each word _____ times.
_____ Learn the definition of each word.
_____ Write a sentence for each word.
_____ Make up a story using some of the words from the puzzle.
_____ Draw pictures of some of the words from the puzzle.
_____ Play "I Spy." Look around the classroom and find the words or the objects they represent.

_____ .

Answer: _____

Answer: _____

Answer: _____

Answer: _____

Name _____   Date _____

WORD CIRCLES

/K/ FINAL POSITION

FIND EVERY THIRD LETTER to find out what the puzzle says. Start at the arrow.

_____ Say each word _____ times.
_____ Learn the definition of each word.
_____ Write a sentence for each word.
_____ Make up a story using some of the words from the puzzle.
_____ Draw pictures of some of the words from the puzzle.
_____ Play "I Spy." Look around the classroom and find the words or the objects they
_____ represent.

_____ _____ .

Answer: _____

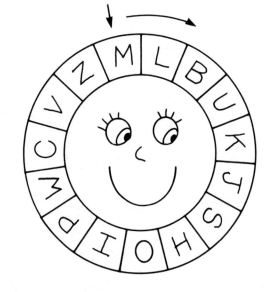

Answer: _____

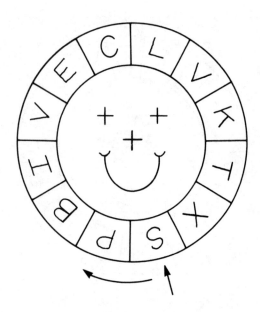

Answer: _____

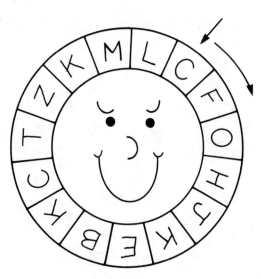

Answer: _____

Name _____   Date _____

DOTTED WORDS

/K/ INITIAL POSITION

COLOR THE DOTTED LETTERS to find the words.

_____ Say each word _____ times.
_____ Learn the definition of each word.
_____ Write a sentence for each word.
_____ Make up a story using one or both of the words from the puzzle.
_____ Draw pictures of one or both of the words from the puzzle.
_____ Play "I Spy." Look around the classroom and find the words or the objects they represent.

_____ _____ .

ANSWERS: _____   _____

Name _____ Date _____

DOTTED WORDS

/K/ MEDIAL POSITION

COLOR THE DOTTED LETTERS to find the words.

_____ Say each word _____ times.
_____ Learn the definition of each word.
_____ Write a sentence for each word.
_____ Make up a story using one or both of the words from the puzzle.
_____ Draw pictures of one or both of the words from the puzzle.
_____ Play "I Spy." Look around the classroom and find the words or the objects they represent.

_____ _____ .

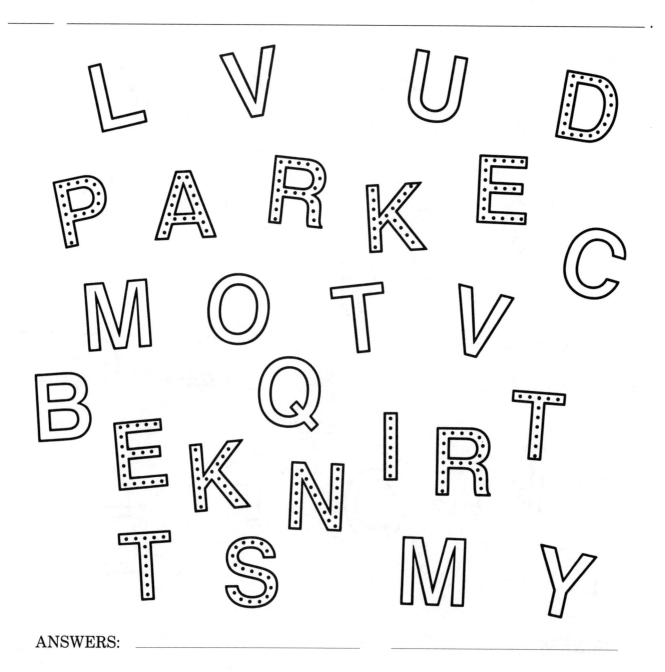

ANSWERS: _____

DOTTED WORDS

/K/ FINAL POSITION

COLOR THE DOTTED LETTERS to find the words.

_____ Say each word _____ times.
_____ Learn the definition of each word.
_____ Write a sentence for each word.
_____ Make up a story using one or both of the words from the puzzle.
_____ Draw pictures of one or both of the words from the puzzle.
_____ Play "I Spy." Look around the classroom and find the words or the objects they
      represent.

_____ .

ANSWERS: _____

SECRET CODES

/K/ INITIAL POSITION

USE THE SECRET CODE TO SOLVE THE CODED WORDS. The answers are found at the bottom of this page in the Word Box.

_____ Say each word _____ times.
_____ Learn the definition of each word.
_____ Write a sentence for each word.
_____ Make up a story using some of the words from the puzzle.
_____ Draw pictures of some of the words from the puzzle.
_____ Play "I Spy." Look around the classroom and find the words or the objects they represent.

_____ _____ .

•SECRET CODE•

A	B	C	D	E	F	G	H	I	J	K
5	10	15	20	25	30	35	40	45	50	55

L	M	N	O	P	Q	R	S	T	U	V
60	65	70	75	80	85	90	95	100	105	110

W	X	Y	Z
115	120	125	130

---

1. 15 75 75 55
    __ __ __ __

2. 15 5 10 45 70
    __ __ __ __ __

3. 55 25 100 100 60 25
    __ __ __ __ __ __

4. 15 5 60 60
    __ __ __ __

5. 15 5 100 100 60 25
    __ __ __ __ __ __

6. 15 75 70 20 45 100 45 75 70
    __ __ __ __ __ __ __ __ __

7. 15 5 30 30 25 45 70 25
    __ __ __ __ __ __ __ __

8. 55 25 125 40 75 60 25
    __ __ __ __ __ __ __

9. 15 75 60 75 90 30 105 60
    __ __ __ __ __ __ __ __

10. 15 5 10 45 70 25 100
    __ __ __ __ __ __ __

•WORD BOX•

CABIN	CAFFEINE	CATTLE	CONDITION	KETTLE
CABINET	CALL	COLORFUL	COOK	KEYHOLE

Name _____   Date _____

SECRET CODES

/K/ MEDIAL POSITION

USE THE SECRET CODE TO SOLVE THE CODED WORDS. The answers are found at the bottom of this page in the Word Box.

_____ Say each word _____ times.
_____ Learn the definition of each word.
_____ Write a sentence for each word.
_____ Make up a story using some of the words from the puzzle.
_____ Draw pictures of some of the words from the puzzle.
_____ Play "I Spy." Look around the classroom and find the words or the objects they represent.

_____ _____ .

•SECRET CODE•

A	B	C	D	E	F	G	H	I	J	K
5	10	15	20	25	30	35	40	45	50	55

L	M	N	O	P	Q	R	S	T	U	V
60	65	70	75	80	85	90	95	100	105	110

W	X	Y	Z
115	120	125	130

---

1. 70 5 80 55 45 70
   ___ ___ ___ ___ ___ ___

2. 10 5 55 25 90
   ___ ___ ___ ___ ___

3. 90 25 15 75 110 25 90
   ___ ___ ___ ___ ___ ___ ___

4. 15 90 5 15 55 25 90
   ___ ___ ___ ___ ___ ___ ___

5. 10 75 10 15 5 100
   ___ ___ ___ ___ ___ ___

6. 65 5 15 5 90 75 70 45
   ___ ___ ___ ___ ___ ___ ___ ___

7. 95 25 5 15 75 5 95 100
   ___ ___ ___ ___ ___ ___ ___ ___

8. 25 15 40 75
   ___ ___ ___ ___

9. 5 15 70 25
   ___ ___ ___ ___

10. 60 75 15 55 25 100
    ___ ___ ___ ___ ___ ___

•WORD BOX•

ACNE	BAKER	ECHO	MACARONI	RECOVER
BOBCAT	CRACKER	LOCKET	NAPKIN	SEACOAST

SECRET CODES

/K/ FINAL POSITION

USE THE SECRET CODE TO SOLVE THE CODED WORDS. The answers are found at the bottom of this page in the Word Box.

_____ Say each word _____ times.
_____ Learn the definition of each word.
_____ Write a sentence for each word.
_____ Make up a story using some of the words from the puzzle.
_____ Draw pictures of some of the words from the puzzle.
_____ Play "I Spy." Look around the classroom and find the words or the objects they represent.

_____ _____ .

```
•SECRET CODE•
A     B     C     D     E     F     G     H     I     J     K
5     10    15    20    25    30    35    40    45    50    55
L     M     N     O     P     Q     R     S     T     U     V
60    65    70    75    80    85    90    95    100   105   110
W     X     Y     Z
115   120   125   130
```

1. 25   5   90   5   15   40   25
___ ___ ___ ___ ___ ___ ___

6. 125   75   60   55
___ ___ ___ ___

2. 100   25   90   90   45   30   45   15
___ ___ ___ ___ ___ ___ ___ ___

7. 100   40   45   15   55
___ ___ ___ ___ ___

3. 30   90   5   70   100   45   15
___ ___ ___ ___ ___ ___ ___

8. 15   90   45   100   45   15
___ ___ ___ ___ ___ ___

4. 95   100   45   15   55
___ ___ ___ ___ ___

9. 95   100   5   100   45   15
___ ___ ___ ___ ___ ___

5. 5   100   40   60   25   100   45   15
___ ___ ___ ___ ___ ___ ___ ___

10. 5   60   45   55   25
___ ___ ___ ___ ___

```
•WORD BOX•
ALIKE        CRITIC       FRANTIC      STICK        THICK
ATHLETIC     EARACHE      STATIC       TERRIFIC     YOLK
```

Name _____ Date _____

SCRAMBLED WORDS

/K/ INITIAL POSITION

UNSCRAMBLE THE WORDS. The answers are in the Word Box.

_____ Say each word _____ times.
_____ Learn the definition of each word.
_____ Write a sentence for each word.
_____ Make up a story using some of the words from the puzzle.
_____ Draw pictures of some of the words from the puzzle.
_____ Play "I Spy." Look around the classroom and find the words or the objects they represent.

_____ _____ .

1. SCOOURETU   _____
2. SCOURIU   _____
3. GKDNRRNTIEAE   _____
4. CGAHUT   _____
5. KETI   _____
6. KEEOLHY   _____
7. CFOEFE   _____
8. KTITNE   _____
9. CNIO   _____
10. GOCUH   _____
11. DINK   _____
12. DNKIEL   _____
13. SIKS   _____
14. SCNOVRETANOI   _____
15. TENBICA   _____

•WORD BOX•

CABINET	COIN	COURTEOUS	KIND	KISS
CAUGHT	CONVERSATION	CURIOUS	KINDERGARTEN	KITE
COFFEE	COUGH	KEYHOLE	KINDLE	KITTEN

Name _____   Date _____

SCRAMBLED WORDS

/K/ MEDIAL POSITION

UNSCRAMBLE THE WORDS. The answers are in the Word Box.

_____ Say each word _____ times.
_____ Learn the definition of each word.
_____ Write a sentence for each word.
_____ Make up a story using some of the words from the puzzle.
_____ Draw pictures of some of the words from the puzzle.
_____ Play "I Spy." Look around the classroom and find the words or the objects they
        represent.

_____ _____ .

1. BKIAGN   _____

2. KTECAJ   _____

3. KGBRAOCUDN   _____

4. KRSNEAES   _____

5. CEBSAEU   _____

6. OKOILGN   _____

7. OKOCNIG   _____

8. ABNOC   _____

9. ANEC   _____

10. HCKICEN   _____

11. NITOCAVA   _____

12. FARYCTO   _____

13. OLACITNO   _____

14. NORIACAM   _____

15. CILOPTERHE   _____

•WORD BOX•

ACNE	BAKING	COOKING	JACKET	MACARONI
BACKGROUND	BECAUSE	FACTORY	LOCATION	SNEAKERS
BACON	CHICKEN	HELICOPTER	LOOKING	VACATION

Name _____   Date _____

SCRAMBLED WORDS

/K/ FINAL POSITION

UNSCRAMBLE THE WORDS. The answers are in the Word Box.

_____ Say each word _____ times.
_____ Learn the definition of each word.
_____ Write a sentence for each word.
_____ Make up a story using some of the words from the puzzle.
_____ Draw pictures of some of the words from the puzzle.
_____ Play "I Spy." Look around the classroom and find the words or the objects they represent.

_____ _____ .

1. RATIHTMECI _____

2. THTKCIPOO _____

3. NAKES _____

4. KACEPUC _____

5. KISC _____

6. KAWEA _____

7. KUDC _____

8. HASTOCM _____

9. KCIHC _____

10. FICRIRET _____

11. OKOL _____

12. AWKL _____

13. EKAST _____

14. ERABK _____

15. OOKLCC _____

•WORD BOX•				
ARITHMETIC	CHICK	LOOK	SNAKE	TERRIFIC
AWAKE	CUPCAKE	O'CLOCK	STEAK	TOOTHPICK
BREAK	DUCK	SICK	STOMACH	WALK

WORD FIND

/K/ INITIAL POSITION

FIND THE WORDS IN THE WORD BOX THAT ARE HIDDEN IN THE PUZZLE. They may be hidden down, across, upside down, diagonal, or backwards.

_____ Say each word _____ times.
_____ Learn the definition of each word.
_____ Write a sentence for each word.
_____ Make up a story using some of the words from the puzzle.
_____ Draw pictures of some of the words from the puzzle.
_____ Play "I Spy." Look around the classroom and find the words or the objects they represent.

_____ _____ .

```
C   A   K   E   D   E   L   L   A   C   J   A
C   A   B   L   E   K   O   Q   E   K   P   K
I   K   C   H   T   O   Z   A   K   B   G   I
K   T   K   N   C   R   D   F   I   K   V   L
J   O   K   K   H   A   K   I   S   Y   F   O
D   N   E   S   Y   D   G   U   S   D   N   W
E   N   K   D   E   Z   T   O   E   E   U   A
K   A   K   X   F   C   Y   B   D   M   A   T
O   C   A   D   A   G   E   L   K   O   X   T
O   O   F   C   A   V   I   T   Y   C   M   A
C   K   I   N   G   L   E   M   A   R   A   C
```

•WORD BOX•

CABLE	CARAMEL	COOL
CACTUS	CAVITY	KHAKI
CAKE	COAXED	KILOWATT
CALLED	COMEDY	KING
CANNOT	COOKED	KISSED

Name _____   Date _____

WORD FIND

/K/ MEDIAL POSITION

FIND THE WORDS IN THE WORD BOX THAT ARE HIDDEN IN THE PUZZLE. They may be hidden down, across, upside down, diagonal, or backwards.

_____ Say each word _____ times.
_____ Learn the definition of each word.
_____ Write a sentence for each word.
_____ Make up a story using some of the words from the puzzle.
_____ Draw pictures of some of the words from the puzzle.
_____ Play "I Spy." Look around the classroom and find the words or the objects they represent.

_____ _____ .

```
F  R  U  E  B  Z  X  Q  S  K  Y  T  R  R  X  H  U  S
L  T  J  L  O  T  N  E  D  I  C  C  A  T  D  Q  A  R
P  K  W  T  C  L  S  J  U  T  Z  L  T  M  Y  M  E  W
U  M  I  T  Z  H  U  R  R  I  C  A  N  E  N  V  Z  Q
W  H  U  E  A  P  V  O  V  N  Z  S  B  X  O  O  P  F
K  C  Q  K  M  P  O  C  K  E  T  C  M  C  U  C  V  B
G  T  I  A  B  I  C  K  E  R  A  Q  E  W  Y  A  L  E
S  N  Y  E  N  C  R  A  C  K  E  R  S  A  L  L  Y  K
G  V  B  T  Z  B  E  C  A  M  E  X  G  C  O  I  A  C
S  F  R  A  V  S  N  E  A  K  E  R  S  N  C  Z  O  J
O  B  Y  E  R  W  R  E  K  A  B  W  L  E  O  E  P  D
V  T  N  W  D  S  U  C  C  E  E  D  X  Q  N  Z  I  A
```

•WORD BOX•

ACCIDENT	CRACKERS	SHAKING
ACNE	HURRICANE	SNEAKERS
BAKER	LOCO	SUCCEED
BECAME	POCKET	TEAKETTLE
BICKER	RECOVER	VOCALIZE

Name _____   Date _____

WORD FIND

/K/ FINAL POSITION

FIND THE WORDS IN THE WORD BOX THAT ARE HIDDEN IN THE PUZZLE. They may be hidden down, across, upside down, diagonal, or backwards.

_____ Say each word _____ times.
_____ Learn the definition of each word.
_____ Write a sentence for each word.
_____ Make up a story using some of the words from the puzzle.
_____ Draw pictures of some of the words from the puzzle.
_____ Play "I Spy." Look around the classroom and find the words or the objects they represent.

_____ _____ .

```
A  A  W  L  A  R  T  I  S  T  I  C  Z  D
C  Y  S  O  C  K  Z  D  X  G  I  Y  E  F
A  N  T  I  Q  U  E  F  P  T  Q  F  X  Q
B  V  W  O  K  E  O  K  E  P  O  C  H  Z
Z  M  X  P  M  S  B  M  S  R  D  L  I  E
C  H  E  C  K  X  H  C  H  S  T  E  A  K
U  R  N  L  J  T  K  F  U  T  P  H  O  A
T  Y  T  G  I  G  A  N  T  I  C  V  K  T
Q  O  B  R  O  D  N  E  Q  C  G  I  L  R
P  L  A  Q  U  E  P  U  M  K  J  W  R  E
C  K  T  D  Z  B  W  R  E  C  K  J  N  V
A  Y  S  P  A  T  R  I  O  T  I  C  V  O
```

•WORD BOX•

ANTIQUE	GIGANTIC	STEAK
ARITHMETIC	OVERTAKE	STICK
ARTISTIC	PATRIOTIC	WOKE
CHECK	PLAQUE	WRECK
EPOCH	SOCK	YOLK

Name _____ Date _____

CROSSWORD PUZZLE

/K/ INITIAL POSITION

COMPLETE THE PUZZLE. The answers are in the Word Box.

_____ Say each word _____ times.
_____ Learn the definition of each word.
_____ Write a sentence for each word.
_____ Make up a story using some of the words from the puzzle.
_____ Draw pictures of some of the words from the puzzle.
_____ Play "I Spy." Look around the classroom and find the words or the objects they represent.

_____ .

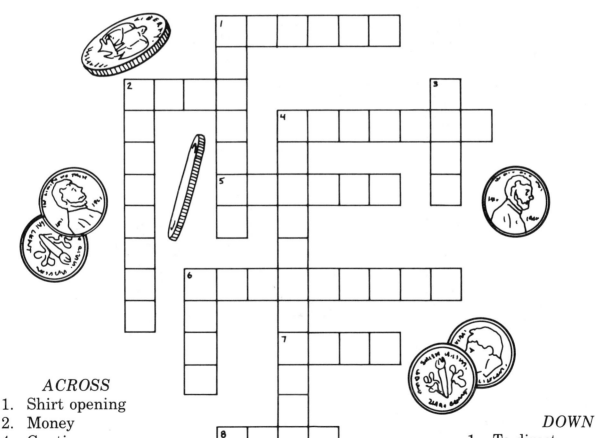

•WORD BOX•

CAREFUL	COLLAR	COMMUNICATE	CUTE	KICK
COIN	COLORFUL	CONDUCT	KEEP	KIDNAPPED
COLA	COMBAT			

ACROSS
1. Shirt opening
2. Money
4. Cautious
5. Battle
6. Abducted
7. Soft drink
8. Hold

DOWN
1. To direct
2. Vivid
3. Pretty
4. To inform
6. To hit with your foot

CROSSWORD PUZZLE

/K/   MEDIAL POSITION

COMPLETE THE PUZZLE. The answers are in the Word Box.

_____ Say each word _____ times.
_____ Learn the definition of each word.
_____ Write a sentence for each word.
_____ Make up a story using some of the words from the puzzle.
_____ Draw pictures of some of the words from the puzzle.
_____ Play "I Spy." Look around the classroom and find the words or the objects they represent.

_____ _____ .

•WORD BOX•

ACORN	BREAKFAST	NAPKIN	POCKET	SECOND
BACON	BROKEN	PECAN	PUMPKIN	SOCCER

ACROSS
1. Container on clothes
2. Morning meal
5. A type of nut
6. Used during a meal
8. A game

DOWN
1. Jack-o'-lantern container
2. Damaged
3. After first
4. Breakfast food
7. A type of nut

Name _____ Date _____

CROSSWORD PUZZLE

/K/ FINAL POSITION

COMPLETE THE PUZZLE. The answers are in the Word Box.

_____ Say each word _____ times.
_____ Learn the definition of each word.
_____ Write a sentence for each word.
_____ Make up a story using some of the words from the puzzle.
_____ Draw pictures of some of the words from the puzzle.
_____ Play "I Spy." Look around the classroom and find the words or the objects they
       represent.

_____ _____ .

```
•WORD BOX•
ATTIC      BRICK      CHALK      OAK           STORYBOOK
BACK       CAKE       KNOCK      RACETRACK     YARDSTICK
```

ACROSS
1. Under the roof of the house
4. A running area
5. Used to tell tales
7. Building materials
8. To hit

DOWN
2. Used to write on a blackboard
3. Measuring tool
6. A type of tree
7. Behind
9. Dessert

ACTIVITIES FOR / L /

121

Name _____   Date _____

WORD CIRCLES

/L/ INITIAL POSITION

FIND EVERY THIRD LETTER to find out what the puzzle says. Start at the arrow.

_____ Say each word _____ times.
_____ Learn the definition of each word.
_____ Write a sentence for each word.
_____ Make up a story using some of the words from the puzzle.
_____ Draw pictures of some of the words from the puzzle.
_____ Play "I Spy." Look around the classroom and find the words or the objects they represent.

_____ _____ .

Answer: _____

Answer: _____

Answer: _____

Answer: _____

Name _____   Date _____

WORD CIRCLES

/L/ MEDIAL POSITION

FIND EVERY THIRD LETTER to find out what the puzzle says. Start at the arrow.

_____ Say each word _____ times.
_____ Learn the definition of each word.
_____ Write a sentence for each word.
_____ Make up a story using some of the words from the puzzle.
_____ Draw pictures of some of the words from the puzzle.
_____ Play "I Spy." Look around the classroom and find the words or the objects they represent.

_____ .

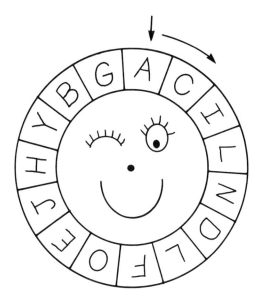

Answer: _____

Answer: _____

Answer: _____   Answer: _____

Name _____ Date _____

WORD CIRCLES

/L/ FINAL POSITION

FIND EVERY THIRD LETTER to find out what the puzzle says. Start at the arrow.

_____ Say each word _____ times.
_____ Learn the definition of each word.
_____ Write a sentence for each word.
_____ Make up a story using some of the words from the puzzle.
_____ Draw pictures of some of the words from the puzzle.
_____ Play "I Spy." Look around the classroom and find the words or the objects they represent.

_____ _____ .

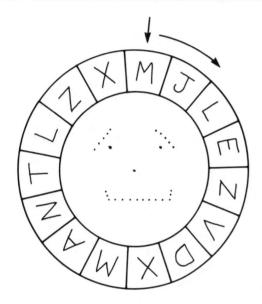

Answer: _____

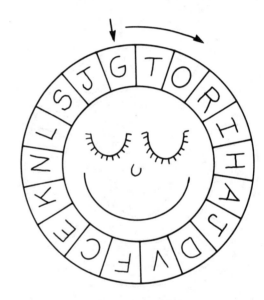

Answer: _____

Answer: _____

Answer: _____

Name _____   Date _____

DOTTED WORDS

/L/ INITIAL POSITION

COLOR THE DOTTED LETTERS to find the words.

_____ Say each word _____ times.
_____ Learn the definition of each word.
_____ Write a sentence for each word.
_____ Make up a story using one or both of the words from the puzzle.
_____ Draw pictures of one or both of the words from the puzzle.
_____ Play "I Spy." Look around the classroom and find the words or the objects they represent.

_____ _____ .

ANSWERS: _____   _____

Name _____ Date _____

DOTTED WORDS

/L/ MEDIAL POSITION

COLOR THE DOTTED LETTERS to find the words.

_____ Say each word _____ times.
_____ Learn the definition of each word.
_____ Write a sentence for each word.
_____ Make up a story using one or both of the words from the puzzle.
_____ Draw pictures of one or both of the words from the puzzle.
_____ Play "I Spy." Look around the classroom and find the words or the objects they represent.

_____ _____ .

ANSWERS: _____ _____

Name _____   Date _____

DOTTED WORDS

/L/ FINAL POSITION

COLOR THE DOTTED LETTERS to find the words.

_____ Say each word _____ times.
_____ Learn the definition of each word.
_____ Write a sentence for each word.
_____ Make up a story using one or both of the words from the puzzle.
_____ Draw pictures of one or both of the words from the puzzle.
_____ Play "I Spy." Look around the classroom and find the words or the objects they
           represent.

_____.

ANSWERS: _____   _____

SECRET CODES

/L/ INITIAL POSITION

USE THE SECRET CODE TO SOLVE THE CODED WORDS. The answers are found at the bottom of this page in the Word Box.

_____ Say each word _____ times.
_____ Learn the definition of each word.
_____ Write a sentence for each word.
_____ Make up a story using some of the words from the puzzle.
_____ Draw pictures of some of the words from the puzzle.
_____ Play "I Spy." Look around the classroom and find the words or the objects they represent.

_____ _____ .

•SECRET CODE•

A	B	C	D	E	F	G	H	I	J	K
7	8	9	10	11	12	13	14	15	16	17

L	M	N	O	P	Q	R	S	T	U	V
18	19	20	21	22	23	24	25	26	27	28

W	X	Y	Z
29	30	31	32

1. 18 15 26 26 11 24
   — — — — — —

2. 18 21 7 12
   — — — —

3. 18 21 27 25 31
   — — — — —

4. 18 7 27 13 14 15 20 13
   — — — — — — — —

5. 18 27 9 17 31
   — — — — —

6. 18 15 26
   — — —

7. 18 7 19 22
   — — — —

8. 18 21 7 20
   — — — —

9. 18 15 17 11 10
   — — — — —

10. 18 27 19 22 31
    — — — — —

•WORD BOX•

LAMP	LIKED	LITTER	LOAN	LUCKY
LAUGHING	LIT	LOAF	LOUSY	LUMPY

Name _____   Date _____

SECRET CODES

/L/ MEDIAL POSITION

USE THE SECRET CODE TO SOLVE THE CODED WORDS. The answers are found at the bottom of this page in the Word Box.

_____ Say each word _____ times.
_____ Learn the definition of each word.
_____ Write a sentence for each word.
_____ Make up a story using some of the words from the puzzle.
_____ Draw pictures of some of the words from the puzzle.
_____ Play "I Spy." Look around the classroom and find the words or the objects they represent.

_____ _____ — .

•SECRET CODE•										
A	B	C	D	E	F	G	H	I	J	K
7	8	9	10	11	12	13	14	15	16	17
L	M	N	O	P	Q	R	S	T	U	V
18	19	20	21	22	23	24	25	26	27	28
W	X	Y	Z							
29	30	31	32							

1. 28 15 21 18 11 20 26
    __ __ __ __ __ __ __

2. 24 11 7 18 15 26 31
    __ __ __ __ __ __ __

3. 7 18 18 11 24 13 31
    __ __ __ __ __ __ __

4. 8 21 29 18 15 20 13
    __ __ __ __ __ __ __

5. 13 7 15 18 31
    __ __ __ __ __

6. 7 18 7 24 19
    __ __ __ __ __

7. 7 8 15 18 15 26 31
    __ __ __ __ __ __ __

8. 9 11 18 18 7 24
    __ __ __ __ __ __

9. 8 15 18 18 15 21 20
    __ __ __ __ __ __ __

10. 27 25 27 7 18 18 31
    __ __ __ __ __ __ __

•WORD BOX•				
ABILITY	ALLERGY	BOWLING	GAILY	USUALLY
ALARM	BILLION	CELLAR	REALITY	VIOLENT

SECRET CODES

/L/ FINAL POSITION

USE THE SECRET CODE TO SOLVE THE CODED WORDS. The answers are found at the bottom of this page in the Word Box.

_____ Say each word _____ times.
_____ Learn the definition of each word.
_____ Write a sentence for each word.
_____ Make up a story using some of the words from the puzzle.
_____ Draw pictures of some of the words from the puzzle.
_____ Play "I Spy." Look around the classroom and find the words or the objects they represent.

_____ _____.

```
•SECRET CODE•
A    B    C    D    E    F    G    H    I    J    K
7    8    9    10   11   12   13   14   15   16   17
L    M    N    O    P    Q    R    S    T    U    V
18   19   20   21   22   23   24   25   26   27   28
W    X    Y    Z
29   30   31   32
```

1. 25 22 21 15 18
    __ __ __ __ __

2. 12 11 11 18
    __ __ __ __

3. 11 23 27 7 18
    __ __ __ __ __

4. 7 29 14 15 18 11
    __ __ __ __ __ __

5. 13 24 7 10 27 7 18
    __ __ __ __ __ __ __

6. 19 27 25 15 9 7 18
    __ __ __ __ __ __ __

7. 12 27 11 18
    __ __ __ __

8. 25 26 31 18 11
    __ __ __ __ __

9. 21 29 18
    __ __ __

10. 9 7 25 27 7 18
    __ __ __ __ __ __

•WORD BOX•

AWHILE	EQUAL	FUEL	MUSICAL	SPOIL
CASUAL	FEEL	GRADUAL	OWL	STYLE

Name _____   Date _____

SCRAMBLED WORDS

/L/ INITIAL POSITION

UNSCRAMBLE THE WORDS. The answers are in the Word Box.

_____ Say each word _____ times.
_____ Learn the definition of each word.
_____ Write a sentence for each word.
_____ Make up a story using some of the words from the puzzle.
_____ Draw pictures of some of the words from the puzzle.
_____ Play "I Spy." Look around the classroom and find the words or the objects they represent.

_____ _____ .

1. NULHC _____

2. TTRLEE _____

3. LABIRRY _____

4. DUALNRY _____

5. ZLAY _____

6. RADLDE _____

7. WALN WOMER _____

8. GELS _____

9. LITONO _____

10. KOOL _____

11. NSOLSE _____

12. MLPU _____

13. YLKCU _____

14. LSTO _____

15. WAL _____

•WORD BOX•				
LADDER	LAWN MOWER	LESSON	LOOK	LUCKY
LAUNDRY	LAZY	LETTER	LOST	LUMP
LAW	LEGS	LIBRARY	LOTION	LUNCH

SCRAMBLED WORDS

/L/ MEDIAL POSITION

UNSCRAMBLE THE WORDS. The answers are in the Word Box.

_____ Say each word _____ times.
_____ Learn the definition of each word.
_____ Write a sentence for each word.
_____ Make up a story using some of the words from the puzzle.
_____ Draw pictures of some of the words from the puzzle.
_____ Play "I Spy." Look around the classroom and find the words or the objects they represent.

_____ _____ .

1. LOCA   _____

2. LYOPONOM   _____

3. LOCOR   _____

4. LANBACE   _____

5. LODLRA   _____

6. LALGROI   _____

7. LANOE   _____

8. LETPEEHNO   _____

9. LECETICR   _____

10. LONLABO   _____

11. LCIHLY   _____

12. MALAR   _____

13. LINGLEMS   _____

14. VELENOPE   _____

15. YFLAIM   _____

•WORD BOX•				
ALARM	BALLOON	COLOR	ENVELOPE	MONOPOLY
ALONE	CHILLY	DOLLAR	FAMILY	SMELLING
BALANCE	COLA	ELECTRIC	GORILLA	TELEPHONE

© 1992 by The Center for Applied Research in Education

Name _____   Date _____

SCRAMBLED WORDS

/L/ FINAL POSITION

UNSCRAMBLE THE WORDS. The answers are in the Word Box.

_____ Say each word _____ times.
_____ Learn the definition of each word.
_____ Write a sentence for each word.
_____ Make up a story using some of the words from the puzzle.
_____ Draw pictures of some of the words from the puzzle.
_____ Play "I Spy." Look around the classroom and find the words or the objects they represent.

_____ _____ .

1. FIRELL _____

2. PNEICL _____

3. BBAALLSKET _____

4. SACSREOEL _____

5. LOVEW _____

6. SLEMUC _____

7. WOLET _____

8. SUGAELL _____

9. ROCOLNT _____

10. WAHLIE _____

11. ABLL _____

12. OHEL _____

13. LIO _____

14. LLAC _____

15. TIAL _____

•WORD BOX•

AWHILE	CALL	HOLE	PENCIL	TAIL
BALL	CASSEROLE	MUSCLE	REFILL	TOWEL
BASKETBALL	CONTROL	OIL	SEA GULL	VOWEL

WORD FIND

/L/ INITIAL POSITION

FIND THE WORDS IN THE WORD BOX THAT ARE HIDDEN IN THE PUZZLE. They may be hidden down, across, upside down, diagonal, or backwards.

_____ Say each word _____ times.
_____ Learn the definition of each word.
_____ Write a sentence for each word.
_____ Make up a story using some of the words from the puzzle.
_____ Draw pictures of some of the words from the puzzle.
_____ Play "I Spy." Look around the classroom and find the words or the objects they represent.

_____ _____ .

```
R  I  L  E  S  S  O  N  B  N  T
N  L  R  C  E  F  I  L  F  A  X
O  T  L  V  C  R  U  H  D  L  N
I  S  G  T  E  C  L  R  L  O  Z
T  A  T  K  K  O  E  L  I  K  E
O  I  C  Q  W  D  I  L  O  L  L
L  O  B  D  D  S  E  O  L  Z  T
L  J  U  A  T  M  L  I  A  R  T
C  O  L  E  O  F  P  Q  D  K  I
L  A  N  N  C  H  K  M  Y  G  L
```

•WORD BOX•

LADDER	LIFE	LOCKER
LADY	LIKE	LOOK
LEMON	LION	LOTION
LESSON	LIP	LOUD
LIAR	LISTEN	LOW
LID	LITTLE	LUCK

Name _____   Date _____

WORD FIND

/L/ MEDIAL POSITION

FIND THE WORDS IN THE WORD BOX THAT ARE HIDDEN IN THE PUZZLE. They may be hidden down, across, upside down, diagonal, or backwards.

_____ Say each word _____ times.
_____ Learn the definition of each word.
_____ Write a sentence for each word.
_____ Make up a story using some of the words from the puzzle.
_____ Draw pictures of some of the words from the puzzle.
_____ Play "I Spy." Look around the classroom and find the words or the objects they represent.

_____ _____ .

```
H  E  L  L  O  V  B  T  S  L  T
T  Y  E  N  O  L  A  B  C  L  R
E  O  G  D  M  C  F  C  O  V  E
L  T  E  R  I  P  N  O  L  Z  T
E  L  C  A  L  R  E  L  O  O  P
V  E  I  L  L  E  V  O  R  Y  O
I  N  L  L  I  L  E  P  Q  L  C
S  O  O  O  O  U  L  K  M  I  I
I  L  P  D  N  R  E  Q  L  M  L
O  A  M  Y  T  I  L  I  B  A  E
N  I  S  L  A  N  D  L  P  F  H
```

•WORD BOX•

ABILITY	ELEVEN	MILLION
ALONE	FAMILY	POLICE
BALONEY	HELICOPTER	RULER
COLOR	HELLO	TELEVISION
DOLLAR	ISLAND	

WORD FIND

/L/ FINAL POSITION

FIND THE WORDS IN THE WORD BOX THAT ARE HIDDEN IN THE PUZZLE. They may be hidden down, across, upside down, diagonal, or backwards.

_____ Say each word _____ times.
_____ Learn the definition of each word.
_____ Write a sentence for each word.
_____ Make up a story using some of the words from the puzzle.
_____ Draw pictures of some of the words from the puzzle.
_____ Play "I Spy." Look around the classroom and find the words or the objects they represent.

_____ _____ .

```
L  V  B  A  S  E  B  A  L  L  S
R  W  T  B  U  L  R  L  T  L  M
O  L  L  A  M  S  Q  L  Z  I  I
L  C  L  Z  L  L  E  M  S  C  L
L  L  L  L  P  E  D  S  Y  N  E
A  N  E  I  J  L  L  A  B  E  L
D  P  L  L  A  I  M  V  L  P  L
S  E  L  A  E  M  E  L  U  R  L
S  E  F  C  L  L  T  X  L  L  A
S  K  G  L  E  C  N  A  C  D  F
```

┌───┐
| •WORD BOX• |
| ALL   MAIL   SMALL |
| BASEBALL   MEAL   SMELL |
| CANCEL   PENCIL   SMILE |
| FALL   ROLL   SPELL |
| LABEL   SELL |
└───┘

Name _____   Date _____

CROSSWORD PUZZLE

/L/ INITIAL POSITION

COMPLETE THE PUZZLE. The answers are in the Word Box.

_____ Say each word _____ times.
_____ Learn the definition of each word.
_____ Write a sentence for each word.
_____ Make up a story using some of the words from the puzzle.
_____ Draw pictures of some of the words from the puzzle.
_____ Play "I Spy." Look around the classroom and find the words or the objects they represent.

_____.

```
•WORD BOX•

LAKE        LEADER      LIAR        LIKE       LOOT
LATER       LEMONADE    LIBRARIAN   LITTER     LOTION
LAVENDER    LETTER      LIFESAVER   LOITER     LUMBERJACK
```

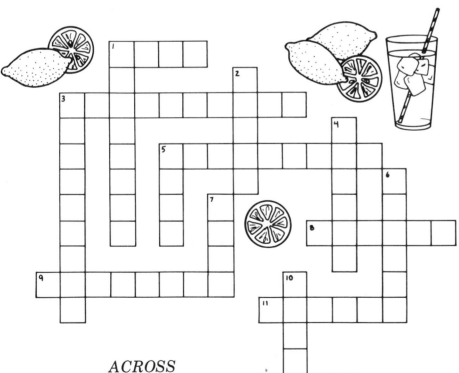

ACROSS
1. Body of water
3. Logger
5. A person or thing that saves people from drowning
8. Message
9. Purple color
11. Linger
12. Rob

DOWN
1. Sour drink
2. After a while
3. A person who works with books
4. Head of a group
5. To prefer
6. Clutter
7. A storyteller of false statements
10. Cream

Name _____   Date _____

CROSSWORD PUZZLE

/L/ MEDIAL POSITION

COMPLETE THE PUZZLE. The answers are in the Word Box.

_____ Say each word _____ times.
_____ Learn the definition of each word.
_____ Write a sentence for each word.
_____ Make up a story using some of the words from the puzzle.
_____ Draw pictures of some of the words from the puzzle.
_____ Play "I Spy." Look around the classroom and find the words or the objects they
          represent.

_____ _____ .

•WORD BOX•

COLOR	HAPPILY	HOLLY	PILLOW	RULER
ELEVATE	HELICOPTER	INTELLIGENT	POLICE	TELEVISION
ELEVEN	HELLO	JELLY	POLITE	

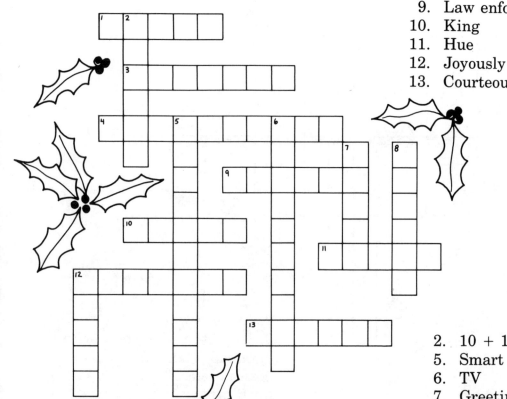

ACROSS

1. Peanut butter and _____
3. To lift
4. Whirlibird
9. Law enforcement officials
10. King
11. Hue
12. Joyously
13. Courteous

DOWN

2. 10 + 1 = _____
5. Smart
6. TV
7. Greeting
8. Headrest
12. The _____ and the ivy

Name _____   Date _____

CROSSWORD PUZZLE

/L/ FINAL POSITION

COMPLETE THE PUZZLE. The answers are in the Word Box.

_____ Say each word _____ times.
_____ Learn the definition of each word.
_____ Write a sentence for each word.
_____ Make up a story using some of the words from the puzzle.
_____ Draw pictures of some of the words from the puzzle.
_____ Play "I Spy." Look around the classroom and find the words or the objects they represent.

_____ _____ .

•WORD BOX•

ALL	CANCEL	FOOTBALL	MEATBALLS	RASCAL
BALL	CONTROL	FUEL	MUSCLE	SWIMMING POOL
BASEBALL	DOLL	MEAL	OATMEAL	TADPOLE
				TALL

ACROSS
1. Breakfast food
4. Spaghetti and _____
6. Gas
7. Baby frog
9. Scoundrel
11. Everyone
13. Round toy
14. Outdoor watering hole

DOWN
2. Dinner
3. Summer sport
4. Brawn
5. Very long
6. Autumn sport
8. Toy
10. Command
12. To stop

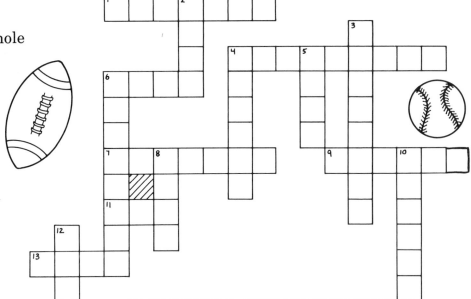

ACTIVITIES FOR /R/

Name _____   Date _____

WORD CIRCLES

/R/ INITIAL POSITION

FIND EVERY THIRD LETTER to find out what the puzzle says. Start at the arrow.

_____ Say each word _____ times.
_____ Learn the definition of each word.
_____ Write a sentence for each word.
_____ Make up a story using some of the words from the puzzle.
_____ Draw pictures of some of the words from the puzzle.
_____ Play "I Spy." Look around the classroom and find the words or the objects they represent.

_____ .

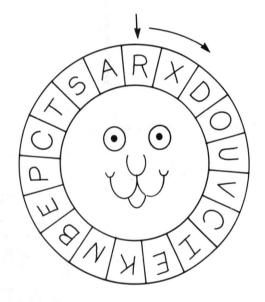

Answer: _____   Answer: _____

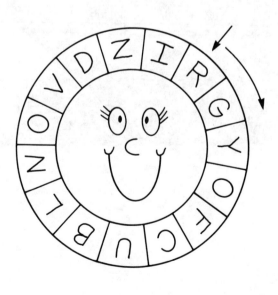

Answer: _____   Answer: _____

Name _____ Date _____

WORD CIRCLES

/R/ MEDIAL POSITION

FIND EVERY THIRD LETTER to find out what the puzzle says. Start at the arrow.

_____ Say each word _____ times.
_____ Learn the definition of each word.
_____ Write a sentence for each word.
_____ Make up a story using some of the words from the puzzle.
_____ Draw pictures of some of the words from the puzzle.
_____ Play "I Spy." Look around the classroom and find the words or the objects they represent.

_____ _____ .

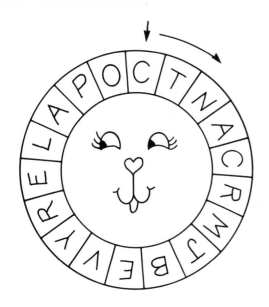

Answer: _____

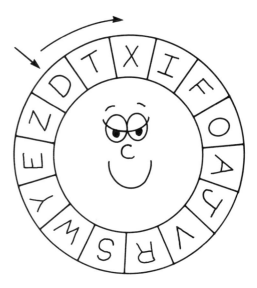

Answer: _____

Answer: _____

Answer: _____

WORD CIRCLES

/R/ FINAL POSITION

FIND EVERY THIRD LETTER to find out what the puzzle says. Start at the arrow.

_____ Say each word _____ times.
_____ Learn the definition of each word.
_____ Write a sentence for each word.
_____ Make up a story using some of the words from the puzzle.
_____ Draw pictures of some of the words from the puzzle.
_____ Play "I Spy." Look around the classroom and find the words or the objects they represent.

_____ _____ .

Answer: _____   Answer: _____

Answer: _____   Answer: _____

Name _____   Date _____

DOTTED WORDS

/R/ INITIAL POSITION

COLOR THE DOTTED LETTERS to find the words.

_____ Say each word _____ times.
_____ Learn the definition of each word.
_____ Write a sentence for each word.
_____ Make up a story using one or both of the words from the puzzle.
_____ Draw pictures of one or both of the words from the puzzle.
_____ Play "I Spy." Look around the classroom and find the words or the objects they represent.

_____ _____ .

ANSWERS: _____   _____

Name _____ Date _____

DOTTED WORDS

/R/ MEDIAL POSITION

COLOR THE DOTTED LETTERS to find the words.

_____ Say each word _____ times.
_____ Learn the definition of each word.
_____ Write a sentence for each word.
_____ Make up a story using one or both of the words from the puzzle.
_____ Draw pictures of one or both of the words from the puzzle.
_____ Play "I Spy." Look around the classroom and find the words or the objects they
         represent.

_____ _____ .

ANSWERS: _____   _____

Name _____ Date _____

DOTTED WORDS

/R/ FINAL POSITION

COLOR THE DOTTED LETTERS to find the words.

_____ Say each word _____ times.
_____ Learn the definition of each word.
_____ Write a sentence for each word.
_____ Make up a story using one or both of the words from the puzzle.
_____ Draw pictures of one or both of the words from the puzzle.
_____ Play "I Spy." Look around the classroom and find the words or the objects they represent.

_____ _____ .

ANSWERS: _____ _____

SECRET CODES

/R/ INITIAL POSITION

USE THE SECRET CODE TO SOLVE THE CODED WORDS. The answers are found at the bottom of this page in the Word Box.

_____ Say each word _____ times.
_____ Learn the definition of each word.
_____ Write a sentence for each word.
_____ Make up a story using some of the words from the puzzle.
_____ Draw pictures of some of the words from the puzzle.
_____ Play "I Spy." Look around the classroom and find the words or the objects they represent.

_____ _____ .

•SECRET CODE•

A	B	C	D	E	F	G	H	I	J	K
1	2	3	4	5	6	7	8	9	10	11
L	M	N	O	P	Q	R	S	T	U	V
12	13	14	15	16	17	18	19	20	21	22
W	X	Y	Z							
23	24	25	26							

---

1. 18 5 10 5 3 20
— — — — — —

2. 18 15 15 6
— — — —

3. 18 5 1 4 25
— — — — —

4. 18 1 7 5
— — — —

5. 18 5 19 20
— — — —

6. 23 18 9 19 20
— — — — —

7. 18 1 9 14 25
— — — — —

8. 23 18 9 20 5 18
— — — — — —

9. 18 5 1 12 12 25
— — — — — —

10. 18 5 7 21 12 1 18
— — — — — — —

•WORD BOX•

RAGE	READY	REGULAR	REST	WRIST
RAINY	REALLY	REJECT	ROOF	WRITER

SECRET CODES

/R/ MEDIAL POSITION

USE THE SECRET CODE TO SOLVE THE CODED WORDS. The answers are found at the bottom of this page in the Word Box.

_____ Say each word _____ times.
_____ Learn the definition of each word.
_____ Write a sentence for each word.
_____ Make up a story using some of the words from the puzzle.
_____ Draw pictures of some of the words from the puzzle.
_____ Play "I Spy." Look around the classroom and find the words or the objects they represent.

_____ _____ .

```
•SECRET CODE•
A    B    C    D    E    F    G    H    I    J    K
1    2    3    4    5    6    7    8    9    10   11
L    M    N    O    P    Q    R    S    T    U    V
12   13   14   15   16   17   18   19   20   21   22
W    X    Y    Z
23   24   25   26
```

1. 16 1 18 1 4 5
    __ __ __ __ __ __

2. 15 18 1 14 7 5
    __ __ __ __ __ __

3. 23 5 1 18 25
    __ __ __ __ __

4. 19 25 18 21 16
    __ __ __ __ __

5. 20 5 18 18 15 18
    __ __ __ __ __ __

6. 19 15 18 18 15 23
    __ __ __ __ __ __

7. 22 5 18 25
    __ __ __ __

8. 1 18 5 1
    __ __ __ __

9. 8 15 18 18 9 2 12 5
    __ __ __ __ __ __ __ __

10. 19 5 18 9 15 21 19
    __ __ __ __ __ __ __

```
•WORD BOX•
AREA          ORANGE        SERIOUS       SYRUP         VERY
HORRIBLE      PARADE        SORROW        TERROR        WEARY
```

Name _____ Date _____

SECRET CODES

/R/ FINAL POSITION

USE THE SECRET CODE TO SOLVE THE CODED WORDS. The answers are found at the bottom of this page in the Word Box.

_____ Say each word _____ times.
_____ Learn the definition of each word.
_____ Write a sentence for each word.
_____ Make up a story using some of the words from the puzzle.
_____ Draw pictures of some of the words from the puzzle.
_____ Play "I Spy." Look around the classroom and find the words or the objects they represent.

_____ _____ .

•SECRET CODE•

A	B	C	D	E	F	G	H	I	J	K
1	2	3	4	5	6	7	8	9	10	11
L	M	N	O	P	Q	R	S	T	U	V
12	13	14	15	16	17	18	19	20	21	22
W	X	Y	Z							
23	24	25	26							

1. 6 9 18 5
    __ __ __ __

2. 2 5 6 15 18 5
    __ __ __ __ __ __

3. 9 7 14 15 18 5
    __ __ __ __ __ __

4. 15 21 20 4 15 15 18
    __ __ __ __ __ __ __

5. 23 8 5 18 5
    __ __ __ __ __

6. 7 21 9 20 1 18
    __ __ __ __ __ __

7. 21 13 16 9 18 5
    __ __ __ __ __ __

8. 3 15 13 16 1 18 5
    __ __ __ __ __ __ __

9. 20 15 21 18
    __ __ __ __

10. 19 15 21 18
    __ __ __ __

•WORD BOX•

BEFORE	FIRE	IGNORE	SOUR	UMPIRE
COMPARE	GUITAR	OUTDOOR	TOUR	WHERE

© 1992 by The Center for Applied Research in Education

SCRAMBLED WORDS

/R/ INITIAL POSITION

UNSCRAMBLE THE WORDS. The answers are in the Word Box.

_____ Say each word _____ times.
_____ Learn the definition of each word.
_____ Write a sentence for each word.
_____ Make up a story using some of the words from the puzzle.
_____ Draw pictures of some of the words from the puzzle.
_____ Play "I Spy." Look around the classroom and find the words or the objects they represent.

_____ _____ .

1. RIWET   _____

2. RAROILAD   _____

3. GRIWGLE   _____

4. GNIR   _____

5. RELXA   _____

6. AIISNR   _____

7. PAWR   _____

8. NORGW   _____

9. NROUD   _____

10. BARBTI   _____

11. IRAOD   _____

12. SERSO   _____

13. TNILGSREW   _____

14. PTRESCE   _____

15. LIDRED   _____

© 1992 by The Center for Applied Research in Education

•WORD BOX•

RABBIT	RAISIN	RIDDLE	ROUND	WRIGGLE
RADIO	RELAX	RING	WRAP	WRITE
RAILROAD	RESPECT	ROSES	WRESTLING	WRONG

SCRAMBLED WORDS

/R/ MEDIAL POSITION

UNSCRAMBLE THE WORDS. The answers are in the Word Box.

_____ Say each word _____ times.
_____ Learn the definition of each word.
_____ Write a sentence for each word.
_____ Make up a story using some of the words from the puzzle.
_____ Draw pictures of some of the words from the puzzle.
_____ Play "I Spy." Look around the classroom and find the words or the objects they represent.

_____ _____ .

1. LAASYR   \   _____

2. IIDCTONARY   _____

3. RRIETBEL   _____

4. VCBLRYOAUA   _____

5. OOORRTMW   _____

6. YRREB   _____

7. EORYHT   _____

8. TARYSECRE   _____

9. REMCEONY   _____

10. TORIUMAUDI   _____

11. ANTPER   _____

12. YSRTRA   _____

13. ARAE   _____

14. SEIROLAC   _____

15. DAYEVERY   _____

•WORD BOX•

AREA	CALORIES	EVERYDAY	SECRETARY	THEORY
AUDITORIUM	CEREMONY	PARENT	STARRY	TOMORROW
BERRY	DICTIONARY	SALARY	TERRIBLE	VOCABULARY

SCRAMBLED WORDS

/R/ FINAL POSITION

UNSCRAMBLE THE WORDS. The answers are in the Word Box.

_____ Say each word _____ times.
_____ Learn the definition of each word.
_____ Write a sentence for each word.
_____ Make up a story using some of the words from the puzzle.
_____ Draw pictures of some of the words from the puzzle.
_____ Play "I Spy." Look around the classroom and find the words or the objects they represent.

_____   _____ .

1. IDONASRU   _____
2. OSRORET   _____
3. SIDAPEPAR   _____
4. KCORRE   _____
5. YNAHWERE   _____
6. TRIWRE   _____
7. RRLEU   _____
8. RAE   _____
9. ARTS   _____
10. WHERESOME   _____
11. EARH   _____
12. ISR   _____
13. UYRO   _____
14. EORGNI   _____
15. FAER   _____

•WORD BOX•				
ANYWHERE	EAR	IGNORE	RULER	STAR
DINOSAUR	FEAR	ROCKER	SIR	WRITER
DISAPPEAR	HEAR	ROOSTER	SOMEWHERE	YOUR

WORD FIND

/R/ INITIAL POSITION

FIND THE WORDS IN THE WORD BOX THAT ARE HIDDEN IN THE PUZZLE. They may be hidden down, across, upside down, diagonal, or backwards.

_____ Say each word _____ times.
_____ Learn the definition of each word.
_____ Write a sentence for each word.
_____ Make up a story using some of the words from the puzzle.
_____ Draw pictures of some of the words from the puzzle.
_____ Play "I Spy." Look around the classroom and find the words or the objects they represent.

_____ _____ .

```
Q  D  H  P  C  Z  D  V  R  W  M
N  T  I  B  B  A  R  N  W  R  L
R  Y  A  O  T  U  M  O  R  O  L
Y  V  R  S  N  J  B  E  Z  N  N
D  R  E  G  T  N  D  H  D  G  O
A  R  Z  O  I  D  A  R  A  R  S
E  I  B  A  T  E  K  C  O  R  A
R  O  R  E  A  L  L  Y  R  C  E
R  W  R  I  T  E  Z  B  F  K  R
V  D  C  A  R  E  V  O  M  E  R
```

•WORD BOX•

RABBIT	REASON	ROBOT
RADIO	RED	ROCKET
RAINBOW	REMOVE	RUN
READY	REST	WRITE
REALLY	ROAD	WRONG

Name _____   Date _____

WORD FIND

/R/ MEDIAL POSITION

FIND THE WORDS IN THE WORD BOX THAT ARE HIDDEN IN THE PUZZLE. They
may be hidden down, across, upside down, diagonal, or backwards.

_____ Say each word _____ times.
_____ Learn the definition of each word.
_____ Write a sentence for each word.
_____ Make up a story using some of the words from the puzzle.
_____ Draw pictures of some of the words from the puzzle.
_____ Play "I Spy." Look around the classroom and find the words or the objects they
        represent.

_____ _____ .

```
E   V   E   R   Y   O   N   E   F   D   K
A   Z   E   J   L   A   H   Y   Y   E   A
R   R   L   R   R   R   R   V   R   G   X
L   E   B   E   T   O   H   R   R   A   N
Y   G   I   V   T   U   E   R   O   I   E
P   N   R   S   B   N   R   O   S   R   R
Q   A   R   M   G   D   O   S   D   R   I
R   R   E   G   O   R   I   L   L   A   S
Z   O   T   S   E   R   O   F   C   M   B
D   I   C   T   I   O   N   A   R   Y   N
R   O   L   A   E   R   E   C   A   V   Y
```

•WORD BOX•		
ARM	EVERYONE	ORANGE
AROUND	FOREST	SIREN
CEREAL	GORILLA	SORRY
DICTIONARY	HERO	STORY
EARLY	MARRIAGE	TERRIBLE

WORD FIND

/R/   FINAL POSITION

FIND THE WORDS IN THE WORD BOX THAT ARE HIDDEN IN THE PUZZLE. They
may be hidden down, across, upside down, diagonal, or backwards.

_____ Say each word _____ times.
_____ Learn the definition of each word.
_____ Write a sentence for each word.
_____ Make up a story using some of the words from the puzzle.
_____ Draw pictures of some of the words from the puzzle.
_____ Play "I Spy." Look around the classroom and find the words or the objects they
represent.

_____ _____ .

```
Y  E  A  R  H  P  B  Q  E
Q  M  R  Z  U  E  Z  R  H
H  D  D  B  F  J  O  A  R
C  G  Y  O  R  T  I  Y  I
E  V  R  I  S  R  N  R  S
R  E  T  G  R  O  O  D  S
U  S  U  U  T  J  X  I  S
S  R  M  I  X  M  V  N  T
D  K  R  T  E  A  R  O  A
M  A  K  A  L  W  C  S  R
E  P  L  R  B  O  R  A  I
R  Q  E  R  A  P  S  U  S
X  O  U  T  D  O  O  R  R
```

•WORD BOX•

BEFORE	GUITAR	STAR
DINOSAUR	HAIR	STIR
DOOR	OUTDOOR	SURE
DRUGSTORE	SIR	TEAR
EAR	SPARE	YEAR

Name _____   Date _____

CROSSWORD PUZZLE

/R/ INITIAL POSITION

COMPLETE THE PUZZLE. The answers are in the Word Box.

_____ Say each word _____ times.
_____ Learn the definition of each word.
_____ Write a sentence for each word.
_____ Make up a story using some of the words from the puzzle.
_____ Draw pictures of some of the words from the puzzle.
_____ Play "I Spy." Look around the classroom and find the words or the objects they
       represent.

_____ _____ .

•WORD BOX•

RAM	RECREATION	REGARD	RELAX	RUG
RAW	RECUR	REGRET	REMARK	RUN
REAR	REFRIGERATE	REGULAR	REPLY	RURAL

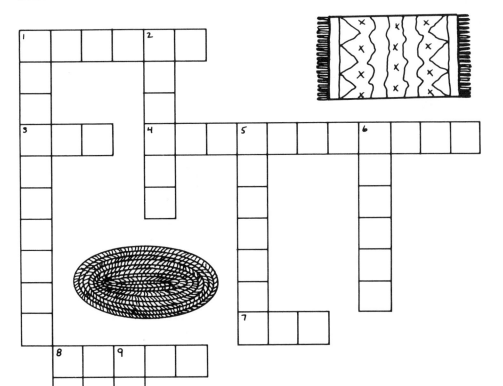

ACROSS
1. Consider
3. Floor covering
4. To cool
7. Hurry
8. Country area
10. Rest

DOWN
1. Entertainment
2. Be sorry for
5. Usual
6. Comment
8. Behind
9. Answer

CROSSWORD PUZZLE

/R/ MEDIAL POSITION

COMPLETE THE PUZZLE. The answers are in the Word Box.

_____ Say each word _____ times.
_____ Learn the definition of each word.
_____ Write a sentence for each word.
_____ Make up a story using some of the words from the puzzle.
_____ Draw pictures of some of the words from the puzzle.
_____ Play "I Spy." Look around the classroom and find the words or the objects they represent.

_____ _____ .

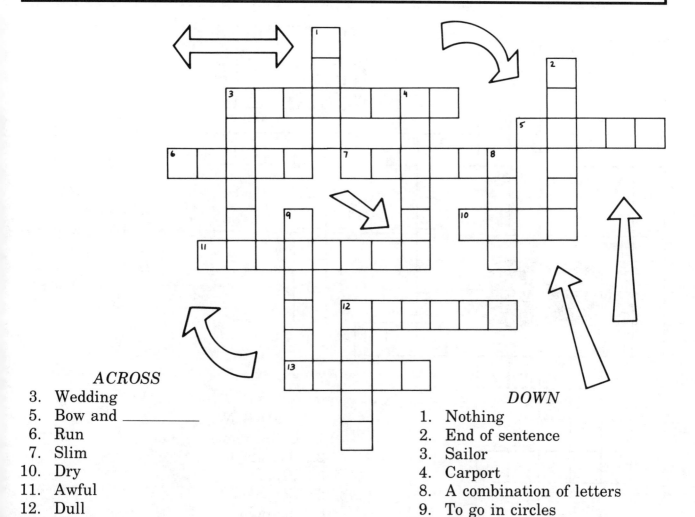

•WORD BOX•

ARID	BERRY	GARAGE	MARRIAGE	TERRIBLE
AROUND	BORING	HURRY	NARROW	WORD
ARROW	DIRTY	MARINE	PERIOD	ZERO

ACROSS
3. Wedding
5. Bow and _____
6. Run
7. Slim
10. Dry
11. Awful
12. Dull
13. Not clean

DOWN
1. Nothing
2. End of sentence
3. Sailor
4. Carport
8. A combination of letters
9. To go in circles
12. Fruit

Name _____   Date _____

CROSSWORD PUZZLE

/R/ FINAL POSITION

COMPLETE THE PUZZLE. The answers are in the Word Box.

_____ Say each word _____ times.
_____ Learn the definition of each word.
_____ Write a sentence for each word.
_____ Make up a story using some of the words from the puzzle.
_____ Draw pictures of some of the words from the puzzle.
_____ Play "I Spy." Look around the classroom and find the words or the objects they represent.

_____ .

•WORD BOX•				
ADORE	DINOSAUR	FOUR	NIGHTMARE	SMEAR
ARE	DOOR	GUITAR	PAIR	SUPPER
BEFORE	EXPLORE	NEAR	PEAR	

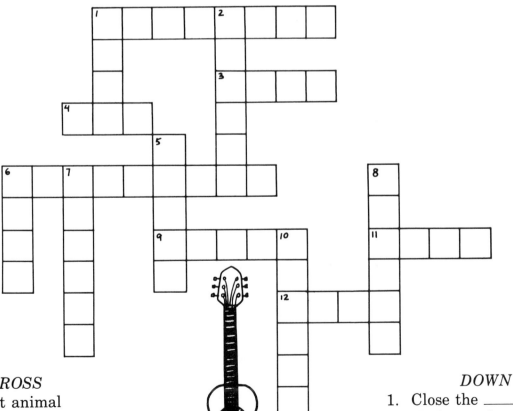

ACROSS

1. Extinct animal
3. Fruit
4. Is—plural
6. Bad dream
9. Cherish
11. Number after 3
12. Two

DOWN

1. Close the _____
2. Night meal
5. Smudge
6. Not far
7. Musical instrument
8. Opposite of after
10. Search

ACTIVITIES FOR /S/

Name _____ Date _____

WORD CIRCLES

/S/ INITIAL POSITION

FIND EVERY THIRD LETTER to find out what the puzzle says. Start at the arrow.

_____ Say each word _____ times.
_____ Learn the definition of each word.
_____ Write a sentence for each word.
_____ Make up a story using some of the words from the puzzle.
_____ Draw pictures of some of the words from the puzzle.
_____ Play "I Spy." Look around the classroom and find the words or the objects they represent.

_____ _____ .

Answer: _____

Answer: _____

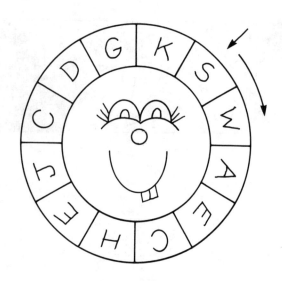

Answer: _____

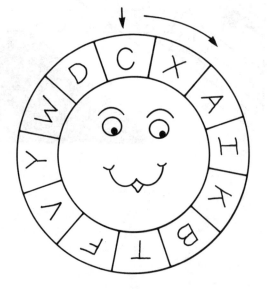

Answer: _____

Name _____   Date _____

WORD CIRCLES

/S/ MEDIAL POSITION

FIND EVERY THIRD LETTER to find out what the puzzle says. Start at the arrow.

_____ Say each word _____ times.
_____ Learn the definition of each word.
_____ Write a sentence for each word.
_____ Make up a story using some of the words from the puzzle.
_____ Draw pictures of some of the words from the puzzle.
_____ Play "I Spy." Look around the classroom and find the words or the objects they
       represent.

_____ _____ .

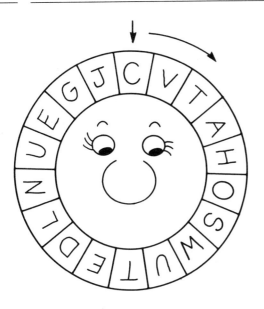

Answer: _____

Answer: _____

Answer: _____

Answer: _____

Name _____ Date _____

WORD CIRCLES

/S/ FINAL POSITION

FIND EVERY THIRD LETTER to find out what the puzzle says. Start at the arrow.

_____ Say each word _____ times.
_____ Learn the definition of each word.
_____ Write a sentence for each word.
_____ Make up a story using some of the words from the puzzle.
_____ Draw pictures of some of the words from the puzzle.
_____ Play "I Spy." Look around the classroom and find the words or the objects they represent.

_____ _____ .

Answer: _____

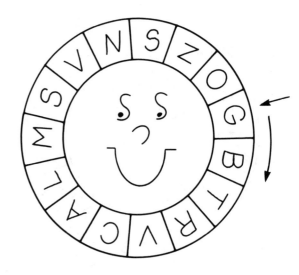

Answer: _____

Answer: _____

Answer: _____

DOTTED WORDS

/S/ INITIAL POSITION

COLOR THE DOTTED LETTERS to find the words.

_____ Say each word _____ times.
_____ Learn the definition of each word.
_____ Write a sentence for each word.
_____ Make up a story using one or both of the words from the puzzle.
_____ Draw pictures of one or both of the words from the puzzle.
_____ Play "I Spy." Look around the classroom and find the words or the objects they represent.

_____ _____ .

ANSWERS: _____ _____

DOTTED WORDS

/S/ MEDIAL POSITION

COLOR THE DOTTED LETTERS to find the words.

_____ Say each word _____ times.
_____ Learn the definition of each word.
_____ Write a sentence for each word.
_____ Make up a story using one or both of the words from the puzzle.
_____ Draw pictures of one or both of the words from the puzzle.
_____ Play "I Spy." Look around the classroom and find the words or the objects they represent.

_____ _____ .

ANSWERS: _____ _____

Name _____ Date _____

DOTTED WORDS

/S/ FINAL POSITION

COLOR THE DOTTED LETTERS to find the words.

_____ Say each word _____ times.
_____ Learn the definition of each word.
_____ Write a sentence for each word.
_____ Make up a story using one or both of the words from the puzzle.
_____ Draw pictures of one or both of the words from the puzzle.
_____ Play "I Spy." Look around the classroom and find the words or the objects they represent.

_____ _____ .

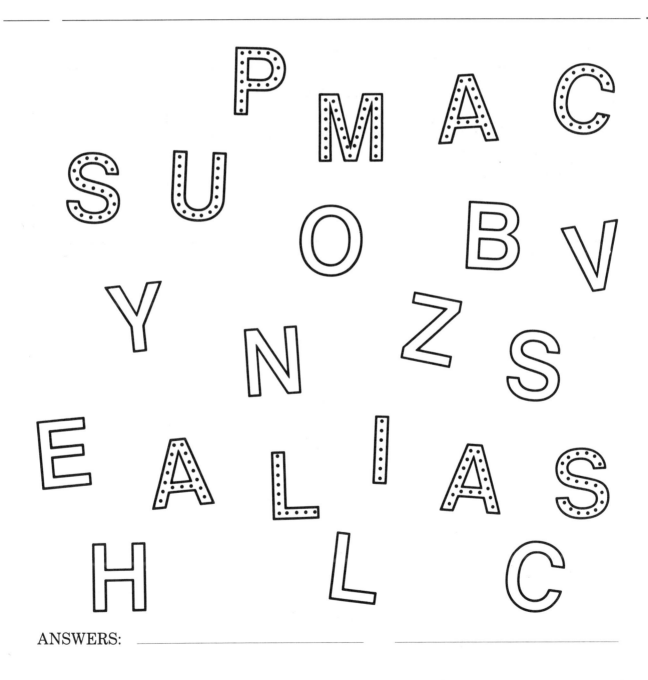

ANSWERS: _____ _____

SECRET CODES

/S/ INITIAL POSITION

USE THE SECRET CODE TO SOLVE THE CODED WORDS. The answers are found at the bottom of this page in the Word Box.

_____ Say each word _____ times.
_____ Learn the definition of each word.
_____ Write a sentence for each word.
_____ Make up a story using some of the words from the puzzle.
_____ Draw pictures of some of the words from the puzzle.
_____ Play "I Spy." Look around the classroom and find the words or the objects they represent.

_____ _____ .

•SECRET CODE•

A	B	C	D	E	F	G	H	I	J	K
26	25	24	23	22	21	20	19	18	17	16
L	M	N	O	P	Q	R	S	T	U	V
15	14	13	12	11	10	9	8	7	6	5
W	X	Y	Z							
4	3	2	1							

1. 8 22 26

   __ __ __

2. 8 26 23

   __ __ __

3. 8 18 20 13

   __ __ __ __

4. 8 22 24 12 13 23

   __ __ __ __ __ __

5. 24 22 15 22 9 2

   __ __ __ __ __ __

6. 24 18 7 2

   __ __ __ __

7. 11 8 2 24 19 18 24

   __ __ __ __ __ __ __

8. 8 26 15 22 8 14 26 13

   __ __ __ __ __ __ __ __

9. 8 22 26 8 19 22 15 15

   __ __ __ __ __ __ __ __

10. 8 2 14 11 26 7 19 2

   __ __ __ __ __ __ __ __

•WORD BOX•

CELERY	PSYCHIC	SALESMAN	SEASHELL	SIGN
CITY	SAD	SEA	SECOND	SYMPATHY

SECRET CODES

/S/ MEDIAL POSITION

USE THE SECRET CODE TO SOLVE THE CODED WORDS. The answers are found at the bottom of this page in the Word Box.

_____ Say each word _____ times.
_____ Learn the definition of each word.
_____ Write a sentence for each word.
_____ Make up a story using some of the words from the puzzle.
_____ Draw pictures of some of the words from the puzzle.
_____ Play "I Spy." Look around the classroom and find the words or the objects they represent.

_____ _____ .

•SECRET CODE•

A	B	C	D	E	F	G	H	I	J	K
26	25	24	23	22	21	20	19	18	17	16
L	M	N	O	P	Q	R	S	T	U	V
15	14	13	12	11	10	9	8	7	6	5
W	X	Y	Z							
4	3	2	1							

1. 26 22 9 12 8 12 15
   __ __ __ __ __ __ __

2. 5 12 18 24 22 8
   __ __ __ __ __ __

3. 23 9 22 8 8 18 13 20
   __ __ __ __ __ __ __ __

4. 25 9 26 24 22 15 22 7
   __ __ __ __ __ __ __ __

5. 24 12 6 9 7 22 8 2
   __ __ __ __ __ __ __ __

6. 25 26 8 18 24
   __ __ __ __ __

7. 24 9 12 8 8 18 13 20
   __ __ __ __ __ __ __ __

8. 25 18 8 12 13
   __ __ __ __ __

9. 25 26 8 18 13
   __ __ __ __ __

10. 18 24 2
    __ __ __

•WORD BOX•

AEROSOL	BASIN	BRACELET	CROSSING	ICY
BASIC	BISON	COURTESY	DRESSING	VOICES

SECRET CODES

/S/ FINAL POSITION

USE THE SECRET CODE TO SOLVE THE CODED WORDS. The answers are found at the bottom of this page in the Word Box.

_____ Say each word _____ times.
_____ Learn the definition of each word.
_____ Write a sentence for each word.
_____ Make up a story using some of the words from the puzzle.
_____ Draw pictures of some of the words from the puzzle.
_____ Play "I Spy." Look around the classroom and find the words or the objects they represent.

_____ _____ .

•SECRET CODE•

A	B	C	D	E	F	G	H	I	J	K
26	25	24	23	22	21	20	19	18	17	16
L	M	N	O	P	Q	R	S	T	U	V
15	14	13	12	11	10	9	8	7	6	5
W	X	Y	Z							
4	3	2	1							

---

1. 12 24 7 12 11 6 8
— — — — — — —

2. 14 22 8 8
— — — —

3. 21 18 9 22 11 15 26 24 22
— — — — — — — — —

4. 25 26 8 8
— — — —

5. 17 6 18 24 22
— — — — —

6. 4 18 7 13 22 8 8
— — — — — — —

7. 25 12 12 16 24 26 8 22
— — — — — — — —

8. 24 15 26 8 8
— — — — —

9. 15 22 7 7 6 24 22
— — — — — — —

10. 24 19 12 9 6 8
— — — — — —

•WORD BOX•

BASS	CHORUS	FIREPLACE	LETTUCE	OCTOPUS
BOOKCASE	CLASS	JUICE	MESS	WITNESS

Name _____ Date _____

SCRAMBLED WORDS

/S/ INITIAL POSITION

UNSCRAMBLE THE WORDS. The answers are in the Word Box.

_____ Say each word _____ times.
_____ Learn the definition of each word.
_____ Write a sentence for each word.
_____ Make up a story using some of the words from the puzzle.
_____ Draw pictures of some of the words from the puzzle.
_____ Play "I Spy." Look around the classroom and find the words or the objects they represent.

_____ _____ .

1. DASDLE   _____

2. LCERIC   _____

3. PUSRE   _____

4. ICTINEZ   _____

5. OLOS   _____

6. LOSTUION   _____

7. DISEKALW   _____

8. NUSNY   _____

9. SHSEAELL   _____

10. LEICNGI   _____

11. USNURBN   _____

12. LARECE   _____

13. ESINR   _____

14. YURSP   _____

15. RSPOONA   _____

•WORD BOX•				
CEILING	CITIZEN	SIDEWALK	SOLUTION	SUNNY
CEREAL	SADDLE	SIREN	SOPRANO	SUPER
CIRCLE	SEASHELL	SOLO	SUNBURN	SYRUP

Name _____   Date _____

SCRAMBLED WORDS

/S/ MEDIAL POSITION

UNSCRAMBLE THE WORDS. The answers are in the Word Box.

_____ Say each word _____ times.
_____ Learn the definition of each word.
_____ Write a sentence for each word.
_____ Make up a story using some of the words from the puzzle.
_____ Draw pictures of some of the words from the puzzle.
_____ Play "I Spy." Look around the classroom and find the words or the objects they represent.

_____ _____ .

1. CRBAETEL   _____

2. SSSGLAE   _____

3. NINOECNT   _____

4. OFIFRCE   _____

5. CENSESRAY   _____

6. REARES   _____

7. ROLESECAS   _____

8. BYBATIS   _____

9. SORECONIHR   _____

10. SBEDIE   _____

11. RCPEIE   _____

12. CMILAED   _____

13. CIIELC   _____

14. CIDIENEM   _____

15. CITYELECTRI   _____

•WORD BOX•

BABYSIT	CASSEROLE	ERASER	INNOCENT	OFFICER
BESIDE	DECIMAL	GLASSES	MEDICINE	RECIPE
BRACELET	ELECTRICITY	ICICLE	NECESSARY	RHINOCEROS

SCRAMBLED WORDS

/S/ FINAL POSITION

UNSCRAMBLE THE WORDS. The answers are in the Word Box.

_____ Say each word _____ times.
_____ Learn the definition of each word.
_____ Write a sentence for each word.
_____ Make up a story using some of the words from the puzzle.
_____ Draw pictures of some of the words from the puzzle.
_____ Play "I Spy." Look around the classroom and find the words or the objects they represent.

_____ _____ .

1. CEAF _____

2. SASLC _____

3. SUB _____

4. CARE _____

5. ISS _____

6. RUSOHC _____

7. LICEDIOUS _____

8. NESSE _____

9. OFIFEC _____

10. CIERP _____

11. NECEACLK _____

12. OPIELC _____

13. LWASUR _____

14. CRTACEPI _____

15. DSOAI _____

•WORD BOX•				
ADIOS	CLASS	NECKLACE	PRACTICE	SENSE
BUS	DELICIOUS	OFFICE	PRICE	SIS
CHORUS	FACE	POLICE	RACE	WALRUS

WORD FIND

/S/ INITIAL POSITION

FIND THE WORDS IN THE WORD BOX THAT ARE HIDDEN IN THE PUZZLE. They
may be hidden down, across, upside down, diagonal, or backwards.

_____ Say each word _____ times.
_____ Learn the definition of each word.
_____ Write a sentence for each word.
_____ Make up a story using some of the words from the puzzle.
_____ Draw pictures of some of the words from the puzzle.
_____ Play "I Spy." Look around the classroom and find the words or the objects they
        represent.

_____ _____ .

```
L  L  E  H  S  A  E  S  T  S
S  S  R  P  A  O  S  E  R  S
U  G  N  O  S  O  U  R  P  N
N  T  A  C  E  A  O  V  M  U
S  A  W  E  E  T  N  E  S  S
H  R  E  L  M  B  Z  D  E  A
I  E  L  E  F  S  S  A  L  T
N  P  C  R  U  K  I  H  L  N
E  U  R  Y  D  A  L  A  S  A
Z  S  I  L  J  I  L  X  C  S
S  S  C  I  T  Y  Y  G  S  A
```

•WORD BOX•

CELERY	SEASHELL	SOAP
CIRCLE	SEEM	SONG
CITY	SELL	SOUR
SALAD	SENT	SUN
SALT	SERVE	SUNSHINE
SANTA	SILLY	SUPER
SAW	SO	

WORD FIND

/S/ MEDIAL POSITION

FIND THE WORDS IN THE WORD BOX THAT ARE HIDDEN IN THE PUZZLE. They may be hidden down, across, upside down, diagonal, or backwards.

_____ Say each word _____ times.
_____ Learn the definition of each word.
_____ Write a sentence for each word.
_____ Make up a story using some of the words from the puzzle.
_____ Draw pictures of some of the words from the puzzle.
_____ Play "I Spy." Look around the classroom and find the words or the objects they represent.

_____ _____.

```
N  E  T  S  I  L  S  T  O  Z  M
P  D  L  O  L  A  S  S  O  E  V
O  I  E  R  B  I  C  Y  C  L  E
S  S  N  E  M  F  R  G  R  C  Q
S  E  I  C  H  L  A  X  U  Y  Z
U  B  L  O  L  E  C  J  D  C  G
M  E  O  N  A  S  I  D  E  I  N
J  R  S  I  F  Y  N  C  T  R  I
S  A  A  H  K  M  G  N  L  T  S
A  S  G  R  L  D  P  I  S  B  S
R  E  D  I  N  O  S  A  U  R  I
B  R  D  R  E  S  S  E  R  Y  M
K  A  Z  W  O  B  S  S  T  S  Q
A  F  S  F  A  U  C  E  T  A  Z
```

•WORD BOX•		
ASIDE	FAUCET	MYSELF
BESIDE	FOSSIL	POSSUM
BICYCLE	GASOLINE	RACING
DINOSAUR	LASSO	RHINOCEROS
DRESSER	LISTEN	
ERASER	MISSING	

WORD FIND

/S/ FINAL POSITION

FIND THE WORDS IN THE WORD BOX THAT ARE HIDDEN IN THE PUZZLE. They may be hidden down, across, upside down, diagonal, or backwards.

_____ Say each word _____ times.
_____ Learn the definition of each word.
_____ Write a sentence for each word.
_____ Make up a story using some of the words from the puzzle.
_____ Draw pictures of some of the words from the puzzle.
_____ Play "I Spy." Look around the classroom and find the words or the objects they represent.

_____ _____ .

```
R  H  I  N  O  C  E  R  O  S
Q  P  W  A  L  R  U  S  C  T
S  R  J  M  O  U  S  E  J  K
U  A  B  U  S  P  E  E  U  E
P  C  A  M  I  C  C  R  I  S
O  T  S  H  A  I  A  A  C  I
T  I  S  F  O  D  L  C  E  M
C  C  Y  V  T  G  P  E  J  O
O  E  S  U  O  H  B  N  U  R
A  X  D  R  E  S  S  E  B  P
```

•WORD BOX•

BASS	MOUSE	RACE
BUS	OCTOPUS	RHINOCEROS
DRESS	PLACE	SHIPS
HOUSE	PRACTICE	VOICE
JUICE	PROMISE	WALRUS

Name _____ Date _____

CROSSWORD PUZZLE

/S/ INITIAL POSITION

COMPLETE THE PUZZLE. The answers are in the Word Box.

_____ Say each word _____ times.
_____ Learn the definition of each word.
_____ Write a sentence for each word.
_____ Make up a story using some of the words from the puzzle.
_____ Draw pictures of some of the words from the puzzle.
_____ Play "I Spy." Look around the classroom and find the words or the objects they represent.

_____ _____ .

•WORD BOX•				
CENT	SALTERN	SANTA CLAUS	SEEM	SIT
CITY	SANCTUM	SAP	SEVEN	SOUTH
SACK	SANITY	SEANCE	SIGNS	SUPERMARKET

ACROSS
1. Directions
3. Bag
5. To be sane is to have your
   _____.
6. You might see a ghost at this function.
8. Money unit
9. A place where salt is made
10. The fluid part of a plant
11. To appear to be
12. A sacred place

DOWN
1. Number after 6
2. Food store
3. St. Nick
4. Metropolis
7. To cover eggs for hatching
9. Direction

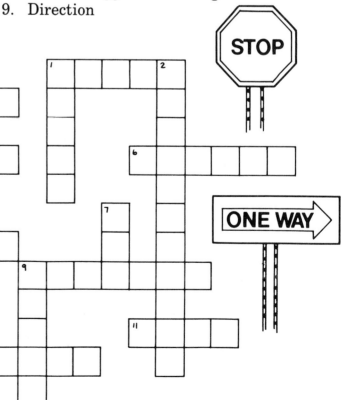

Name _____ Date _____

CROSSWORD PUZZLE

/S/ MEDIAL POSITION

COMPLETE THE PUZZLE. The answers are in the Word Box.

_____ Say each word _____ times.
_____ Learn the definition of each word.
_____ Write a sentence for each word.
_____ Make up a story using some of the words from the puzzle.
_____ Draw pictures of some of the words from the puzzle.
_____ Play "I Spy." Look around the classroom and find the words or the objects they
        represent.

_____ _____ .

```
┌─────────────────────────────────────────────────────────────────────┐
│                          •WORD BOX•                                   │
│  BABYSIT       CLOSER       ICY        MUSCLE       PESO              │
│  BRACELET      FANTASY      LASSO      OFFICER      POSITIVE          │
│  CASTLE        FOSSIL       LESSEN     PARASOL      RECEIPT           │
│  CHASER        GOSSIP       MISSING                                   │
└─────────────────────────────────────────────────────────────────────┘
```

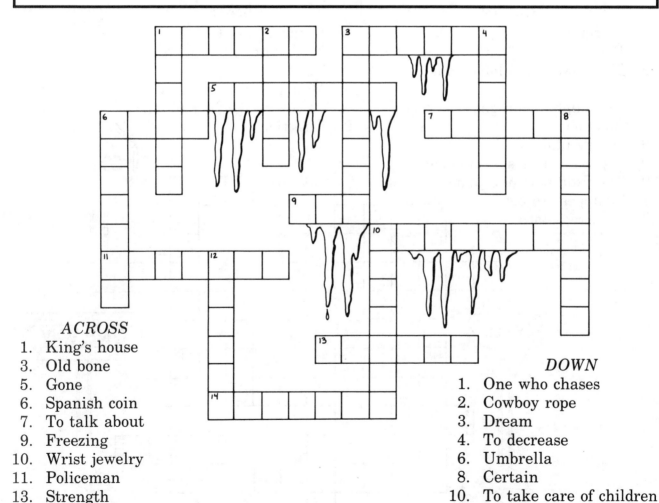

ACROSS
1. King's house
3. Old bone
5. Gone
6. Spanish coin
7. To talk about
9. Freezing
10. Wrist jewelry
11. Policeman
13. Strength
14. Sales ticket

DOWN
1. One who chases
2. Cowboy rope
3. Dream
4. To decrease
6. Umbrella
8. Certain
10. To take care of children
12. Nearer

Name _____   Date _____

CROSSWORD PUZZLE

/S/ FINAL POSITION

COMPLETE THE PUZZLE. The answers are in the Word Box.

_____ Say each word _____ times.
_____ Learn the definition of each word.
_____ Write a sentence for each word.
_____ Make up a story using some of the words from the puzzle.
_____ Draw pictures of some of the words from the puzzle.
_____ Play "I Spy." Look around the classroom and find the words or the objects they represent.

_____ .

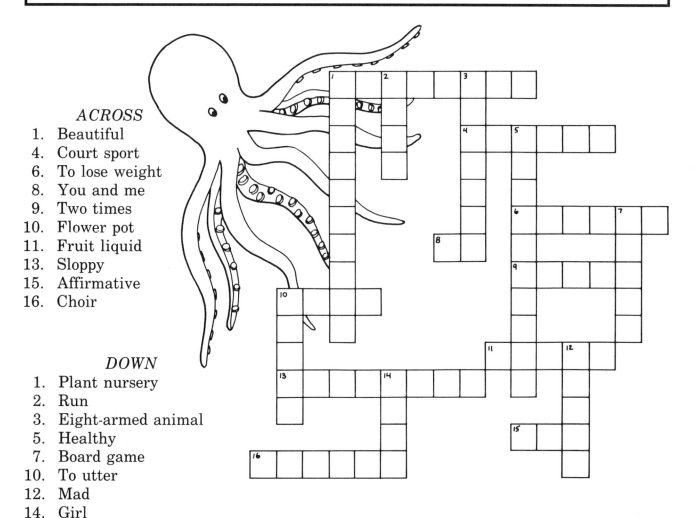

•WORD BOX•

CARELESS	GORGEOUS	NUTRITIOUS	TENNIS	VASE
CHESS	GREENHOUSE	OCTOPUS	TWICE	VOICE
CHORUS	JUICE	RACE	US	YES
CROSS	LASS	REDUCE		

ACROSS
1. Beautiful
4. Court sport
6. To lose weight
8. You and me
9. Two times
10. Flower pot
11. Fruit liquid
13. Sloppy
15. Affirmative
16. Choir

DOWN
1. Plant nursery
2. Run
3. Eight-armed animal
5. Healthy
7. Board game
10. To utter
12. Mad
14. Girl

ACTIVITIES FOR /SH/

WORD CIRCLES

/SH/ INITIAL POSITION

FIND EVERY THIRD LETTER to find out what the puzzle says. Start at the arrow.

_____ Say each word _____ times.
_____ Learn the definition of each word.
_____ Write a sentence for each word.
_____ Make up a story using some of the words from the puzzle.
_____ Draw pictures of some of the words from the puzzle.
_____ Play "I Spy." Look around the classroom and find the words or the objects they
represent.

_____ _____ .

Answer: _____   Answer: _____

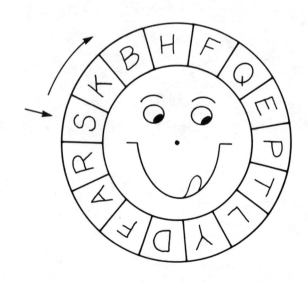

Answer: _____   Answer: _____

Name _____   Date _____

WORD CIRCLES

/SH/ MEDIAL POSITION

FIND EVERY THIRD LETTER to find out what the puzzle says. Start at the arrow.

_____ Say each word _____ times.
_____ Learn the definition of each word.
_____ Write a sentence for each word.
_____ Make up a story using some of the words from the puzzle.
_____ Draw pictures of some of the words from the puzzle.
_____ Play "I Spy." Look around the classroom and find the words or the objects they represent.

_____ _____ .

Answer: _____

Answer: _____

Answer: _____

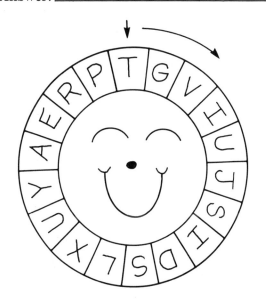

Answer: _____

Name _____   Date _____

WORD CIRCLES

/SH/ FINAL POSITION

FIND EVERY THIRD LETTER to find out what the puzzle says. Start at the arrow.

_____ Say each word _____ times.
_____ Learn the definition of each word.
_____ Write a sentence for each word.
_____ Make up a story using some of the words from the puzzle.
_____ Draw pictures of some of the words from the puzzle.
_____ Play "I Spy." Look around the classroom and find the words or the objects they represent.

_____ _____ .

Answer: _____

Answer: _____

Answer: _____

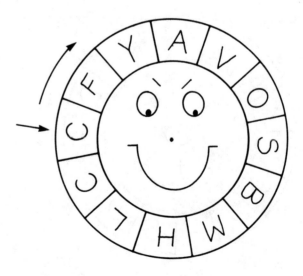

Answer: _____

Name _____   Date _____

DOTTED WORDS

/SH/ INITIAL POSITION

COLOR THE DOTTED LETTERS to find the words.

_____ Say each word _____ times.
_____ Learn the definition of each word.
_____ Write a sentence for each word.
_____ Make up a story using one or both of the words from the puzzle.
_____ Draw pictures of one or both of the words from the puzzle.
_____ Play "I Spy." Look around the classroom and find the words or the objects they
represent.

_____ _____ .

ANSWERS: _____   _____

Name _____ Date _____

DOTTED WORDS

/SH/ MEDIAL POSITION

COLOR THE DOTTED LETTERS to find the words.

_____ Say each word _____ times.
_____ Learn the definition of each word.
_____ Write a sentence for each word.
_____ Make up a story using one or both of the words from the puzzle.
_____ Draw pictures of one or both of the words from the puzzle.
_____ Play "I Spy." Look around the classroom and find the words or the objects they
        represent.

_____ _____ .

ANSWERS: _____   _____

DOTTED WORDS

/SH/ FINAL POSITION

COLOR THE DOTTED LETTERS to find the words.

_____ Say each word _____ times.
_____ Learn the definition of each word.
_____ Write a sentence for each word.
_____ Make up a story using one or both of the words from the puzzle.
_____ Draw pictures of one or both of the words from the puzzle.
_____ Play "I Spy." Look around the classroom and find the words or the objects they represent.

_____ _____ .

K D O F R
F I S H E T
X S
R J B H
T L G P

ANSWERS: _____   Date _____

SECRET CODES

/SH/   INITIAL POSITION

USE THE SECRET CODE TO SOLVE THE CODED WORDS. The answers are found at the bottom of this page in the Word Box.

_____ Say each word _____ times.
_____ Learn the definition of each word.
_____ Write a sentence for each word.
_____ Make up a story using some of the words from the puzzle.
_____ Draw pictures of some of the words from the puzzle.
_____ Play "I Spy." Look around the classroom and find the words or the objects they represent.

_____ _____ .

•SECRET CODE•										
A	B	C	D	E	F	G	H	I	J	K
1	2	3	4	5	6	7	8	9	10	11
L	M	N	O	P	Q	R	S	T	U	V
12	13	14	15	16	17	18	19	20	21	22
W	X	Y	Z							
23	24	25	26							

1. 19 8 1 13 5

   __ __ __ __ __

2. 19 8 15 22 5 12

   __ __ __ __ __ __

3. 19 8 15 23

   __ __ __ __

4. 3 8 9 3

   __ __ __ __

5. 19 8 15 23 5 18

   __ __ __ __ __ __

6. 19 8 1 4 15 23

   __ __ __ __ __ __

7. 19 8 15 21 12 4

   __ __ __ __ __ __

8. 19 8 1 18 11

   __ __ __ __ __

9. 19 21 18 5

   __ __ __ __

10. 19 8 15 15 11

   __ __ __ __ __

•WORD BOX•				
CHIC	SHAME	SHOOK	SHOW	SHOVEL
SHADOW	SHARK	SHOULD	SHOWER	SURE

Name _____   Date _____

SECRET CODES

/SH/ MEDIAL POSITION

USE THE SECRET CODE TO SOLVE THE CODED WORDS. The answers are found at the bottom of this page in the Word Box.

_____ Say each word _____ times.
_____ Learn the definition of each word.
_____ Write a sentence for each word.
_____ Make up a story using some of the words from the puzzle.
_____ Draw pictures of some of the words from the puzzle.
_____ Play "I Spy." Look around the classroom and find the words or the objects they represent.

_____ _____ .

•SECRET CODE•

A	B	C	D	E	F	G	H	I	J	K
1	2	3	4	5	6	7	8	9	10	11

L	M	N	O	P	Q	R	S	T	U	V
12	13	14	15	16	17	18	19	20	21	22

W	X	Y	Z
23	24	25	26

---

1. 3 1 19 8 9 5 18

    __ __ __ __ __ __ __

2. 4 9 19 8 5 19

    __ __ __ __ __ __

3. 19 16 5 3 9 1 12

    __ __ __ __ __ __ __

4. 3 21 19 8 9 15 14

    __ __ __ __ __ __ __

5. 12 15 20 9 15 14

    __ __ __ __ __ __

6. 23 15 18 19 8 9 16

    __ __ __ __ __ __ __

7. 12 21 24 21 18 25

    __ __ __ __ __ __

8. 9 13 9 20 1 20 9 15 14

    __ __ __ __ __ __ __ __ __

9. 12 15 3 1 20 9 15 14

    __ __ __ __ __ __ __ __

10. 19 21 19 16 9 3 9 15 14

    __ __ __ __ __ __ __ __ __

•WORD BOX•

CASHIER	DISHES	LOCATION	LUXURY	SUSPICION
CUSHION	IMITATION	LOTION	SPECIAL	WORSHIP

Name _____   Date _____

SECRET CODES

/SH/ FINAL POSITION

USE THE SECRET CODE TO SOLVE THE CODED WORDS. The answers are found at the bottom of this page in the Word Box.

_____ Say each word _____ times.
_____ Learn the definition of each word.
_____ Write a sentence for each word.
_____ Make up a story using some of the words from the puzzle.
_____ Draw pictures of some of the words from the puzzle.
_____ Play "I Spy." Look around the classroom and find the words or the objects they represent.

_____ _____ .

•SECRET CODE•

A	B	C	D	E	F	G	H	I	J	K
1	2	3	4	5	6	7	8	9	10	11
L	**M**	**N**	**O**	**P**	**Q**	**R**	**S**	**T**	**U**	**V**
12	13	14	15	16	17	18	19	20	21	22
W	**X**	**Y**	**Z**							
23	24	25	26							

---

1. 3 18 21 19 8

— — — — —

2. 19 17 21 1 19 8

— — — — — —

3. 6 9 14 9 19 8

— — — — — —

4. 6 12 1 19 8

— — — — —

5. 23 9 19 8

— — — —

6. 5 25 5 12 1 19 8

— — — — — — —

7. 16 21 19 8

— — — —

8. 8 1 18 19 8

— — — — —

9. 12 9 3 15 18 9 3 5

— — — — — — — —

10. 6 15 15 12 9 19 8

— — — — — — —

•WORD BOX•

CRUSH	FINISH	FOOLISH	LICORICE	SQUASH
EYELASH	FLASH	HARSH	PUSH	WISH

SCRAMBLED WORDS

/SH/ INITIAL POSITION

UNSCRAMBLE THE WORDS. The answers are in the Word Box.

_____ Say each word _____ times.
_____ Learn the definition of each word.
_____ Write a sentence for each word.
_____ Make up a story using some of the words from the puzzle.
_____ Draw pictures of some of the words from the puzzle.
_____ Play "I Spy." Look around the classroom and find the words or the objects they represent.

_____ _____ .

1. EKSAH   _____
2. PHRSA   _____
3. RUAGS   _____
4. TTLESHU   _____
5. YHS   _____
6. ISRHT   _____
7. SEH   _____
8. OSHW   _____
9. EHFC   _____
10. TSOHR   _____
11. HCLATE   _____
12. VHISRE   _____
13. LSOHEV   _____
14. BHYSBA   _____
15. ETSREHL   _____

•WORD BOX•				
CHALET	SHAKE	SHELTER	SHORT	SHUTTLE
CHEF	SHARP	SHIRT	SHOVEL	SHY
SHABBY	SHE	SHIVER	SHOW	SUGAR

Name _____   Date _____

SCRAMBLED WORDS

/SH/ MEDIAL POSITION

UNSCRAMBLE THE WORDS. The answers are in the Word Box.

_____ Say each word _____ times.
_____ Learn the definition of each word.
_____ Write a sentence for each word.
_____ Make up a story using some of the words from the puzzle.
_____ Draw pictures of some of the words from the puzzle.
_____ Play "I Spy." Look around the classroom and find the words or the objects they
       represent.

_____ _____ .

  1. SINGHUP   _____

  2. UINOTCA   _____

  3. RESHWA   _____

  4. IUETSS   _____

  5. NTAOCAVI   _____

  6. ANIOTC   _____

  7. DADNTIIO   _____

  8. BSESHU   _____

  9. NINITCCEHA   _____

10. USMNICIA   _____

11. TCDUEANOI   _____

12. TCIDIONYRA   _____

13. MANERFISH   _____

14. SEHSA   _____

15. CSOALI   _____

•WORD BOX•

ACTION	BUSHES	EDUCATION	PUSHING	TISSUE
ADDITION	CAUTION	FISHERMAN	SOCIAL	VACATION
ASHES	DICTIONARY	MUSICIAN	TECHNICIAN	WASHER

SCRAMBLED WORDS

/SH/ FINAL POSITION

UNSCRAMBLE THE WORDS. The answers are in the Word Box.

_____ Say each word _____ times.
_____ Learn the definition of each word.
_____ Write a sentence for each word.
_____ Make up a story using some of the words from the puzzle.
_____ Draw pictures of some of the words from the puzzle.
_____ Play "I Spy." Look around the classroom and find the words or the objects they represent.

_____ _____ .

1. HSSELIF _____

2. SHUBR _____

3. PLSAHS _____

4. IFHS _____

5. CSAH _____

6. RASTH _____

7. WSAH _____

8. EERHFSR _____

9. SIWH _____

10. PHIUNS _____

11. SHUENISLF _____

12. RTSHOTOHBU _____

13. HSUCR _____

14. LICOCRIE _____

15. DISHAR _____

```
•WORD BOX•
```

BRUSH	FISH	RADISH	SPLASH	UNSELFISH
CASH	LICORICE	REFRESH	TOOTHBRUSH	WASH
CRUSH	PUNISH	SELFISH	TRASH	WISH

WORD FIND

/SH/ INITIAL POSITION

FIND THE WORDS IN THE WORD BOX THAT ARE HIDDEN IN THE PUZZLE. They may be hidden down, across, upside down, diagonal, or backwards.

_____ Say each word _____ times.
_____ Learn the definition of each word.
_____ Write a sentence for each word.
_____ Make up a story using some of the words from the puzzle.
_____ Draw pictures of some of the words from the puzzle.
_____ Play "I Spy." Look around the classroom and find the words or the objects they represent.

_____ _____ .

```
H  Q  S  D  R  E  W  O  H  S  U
H  S  H  V  S  U  R  E  S  S  F
S  S  E  O  C  H  S  H  H  H  N
S  H  N  S  H  Y  I  O  E  A  T
H  A  I  B  E  P  L  V  R  M  E
A  R  H  X  F  K  A  M  S  P  E
R  E  S  A  R  H  S  H  O  O  H
P  E  E  H  S  S  H  O  E  O  S
J  C  T  O  O  H  S  L  V  P  G
X  H  S  P  O  H  S  S  H  O  V
```

•WORD BOX•

CHEF	SHEEP	SHOOT
SHAMPOO	SHEET	SHOP
SHARE	SHINE	SHOWER
SHARP	SHIP	SHY
SHAVE	SHOE	SURE
SHE		

WORD FIND

/SH/ MEDIAL POSITION

FIND THE WORDS IN THE WORD BOX THAT ARE HIDDEN IN THE PUZZLE. They may be hidden down, across, upside down, diagonal, or backwards.

_____ Say each word _____ times.
_____ Learn the definition of each word.
_____ Write a sentence for each word.
_____ Make up a story using some of the words from the puzzle.
_____ Draw pictures of some of the words from the puzzle.
_____ Play "I Spy." Look around the classroom and find the words or the objects they represent.

_____ _____ .

```
V  H  S  O  C  E  A  N  A  S  T
E  E  R  O  H  S  A  E  S  H  R
N  T  I  S  S  U  E  F  P  S  A
O  P  S  E  E  A  I  V  E  N  N
I  T  L  C  J  C  Q  H  C  O  S
T  B  O  T  T  T  S  D  I  I  P
U  X  S  I  U  I  H  O  A  T  O
A  I  O  O  D  O  M  W  L  A  R
C  N  P  N  H  N  T  G  R  T  T
L  M  I  S  S  I  O  N  Z  S  A
S  H  O  N  L  O  T  I  O  N  T
Z  W  R  P  V  C  K  N  F  U  I
H  N  O  I  T  A  P  U  C  C  O
E  B  Y  V  Q  N  O  I  T  O  N
```

+---+
| •WORD BOX• |
| ACTION   MISSION   SECTION |
| CAUTION   NOTION   SPECIAL |
| DISHES   OCCUPATION   STATION |
| FICTION   OCEAN   TISSUE |
| LOTION   SEASHORE   TRANSPORTATION |
+---+

WORD FIND

/SH/ FINAL POSITION

FIND THE WORDS IN THE WORD BOX THAT ARE HIDDEN IN THE PUZZLE. They may be hidden down, across, upside down, diagonal, or backwards.

_____ Say each word _____ times.
_____ Learn the definition of each word.
_____ Write a sentence for each word.
_____ Make up a story using some of the words from the puzzle.
_____ Draw pictures of some of the words from the puzzle.
_____ Play "I Spy." Look around the classroom and find the words or the objects they represent.

_____ _____ .

```
H  S  A  T  R  A  S  H  S  O
E  M  V  S  H  H  A  H  P  T
Y  H  U  S  H  S  W  S  L  Q
E  B  U  H  S  A  D  U  A  H
L  B  W  S  S  N  K  R  S  S
A  L  I  H  M  H  C  B  H  I
S  R  S  F  H  S  I  N  I  F
H  W  H  S  U  U  J  V  P  U
S  H  A  O  P  P  G  L  S  V
S  M  S  E  L  F  I  S  H  C
H  S  I  L  O  O  F  M  Y  F
```

•WORD BOX•

ASH	FISH	SELFISH
BRUSH	FOOLISH	SPLASH
BUSH	HUSH	TRASH
EYELASH	MASH	WASH
FINISH	PUSH	WISH

Name _____   Date _____

CROSSWORD PUZZLE

/SH/ INITIAL POSITION

COMPLETE THE PUZZLE. The answers are in the Word Box.

_____ Say each word _____ times.
_____ Learn the definition of each word.
_____ Write a sentence for each word.
_____ Make up a story using some of the words from the puzzle.
_____ Draw pictures of some of the words from the puzzle.
_____ Play "I Spy." Look around the classroom and find the words or the objects they represent.

_____ _____ .

•WORD BOX•

CHAUFFEUR	SHE	SHIELD	SHIP	SHORT
CHEF	SHEETS	SHIFT	SHOELACE	SHOUT
SHAMPOO	SHERBET	SHINE	SHOOT	SHOW
				SHOWER

ACROSS

1. Use them to tie your shoes
5. A large boat
6. Cook
7. Yell
8. Ice cream
9. To exhibit
10. To glow

DOWN

1. Hair soap
2. Driver
3. Not tall
4. To move
5. To fire
7. Bed linen
8. Rain storm
9. To protect
10. Her

CROSSWORD PUZZLE

/SH/ MEDIAL POSITION

COMPLETE THE PUZZLE. The answers are in the Word Box.

_____ Say each word _____ times.
_____ Learn the definition of each word.
_____ Write a sentence for each word.
_____ Make up a story using some of the words from the puzzle.
_____ Draw pictures of some of the words from the puzzle.
_____ Play "I Spy." Look around the classroom and find the words or the objects they represent.

_____ _____ .

•WORD BOX•

BASHFUL	NATION	OPTION	SECTION	WISHBONE
CAUTION	OCCUPATION	SEASHORE	TENSION	WORSHIP
FASHION	OCEAN			

ACROSS
2. Choice
3. Lucky bone
5. Country
6. Style
9. Warning
10. Career

DOWN
1. By the ocean
2. Sea
3. To adore
4. Shy
7. A part
8. To feel stress

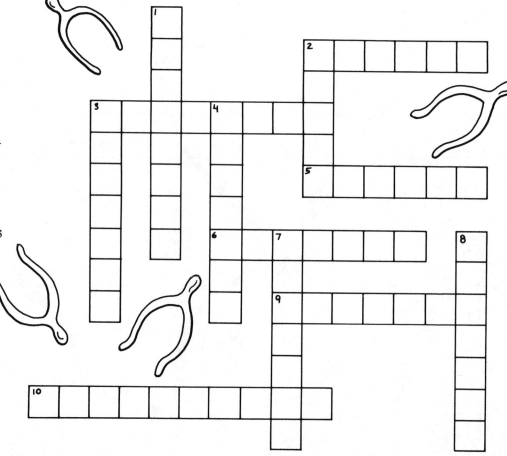

CROSSWORD PUZZLE

/SH/   FINAL POSITION

COMPLETE THE PUZZLE. The answers are in the Word Box.

_____ Say each word _____ times.
_____ Learn the definition of each word.
_____ Write a sentence for each word.
_____ Make up a story using some of the words from the puzzle.
_____ Draw pictures of some of the words from the puzzle.
_____ Play "I Spy." Look around the classroom and find the words or the objects they represent.

_____ .

•WORD BOX•

ACCOMPLISH	GARNISH	HUSH	RADISH	SPLASH
AMBUSH	GASH	PAINTBRUSH	RASH	SQUASH
BRUSH	GOLDFISH	PUSH	RUSH	UNSELFISH
GALOSH	HAIRBRUSH			

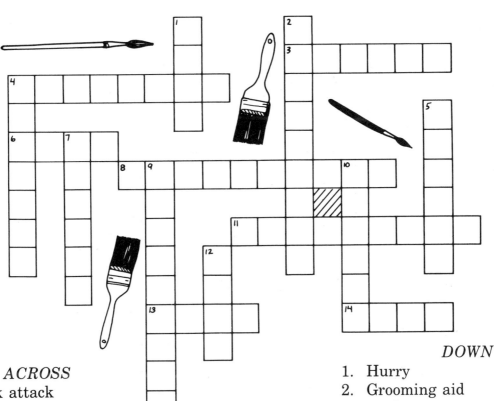

ACROSS

3. Sneak attack
4. An aquarium fish
6. A skin inflammation
8. Tool used for coloring
11. Not stingy
13. To shove
14. Be quiet

DOWN

1. Hurry
2. Grooming aid
4. To decorate
5. A hard, red vegetable
7. A yellow or green vegetable
9. To do
10. To spatter
12. A cut

ACTIVITIES FOR /T/

WORD CIRCLES

/T/ INITIAL POSITION

FIND EVERY THIRD LETTER to find out what the puzzle says. Start at the arrow.

_____ Say each word _____ times.
_____ Learn the definition of each word.
_____ Write a sentence for each word.
_____ Make up a story using some of the words from the puzzle.
_____ Draw pictures of some of the words from the puzzle.
_____ Play "I Spy." Look around the classroom and find the words or the objects they
          represent.

_____ _____ .

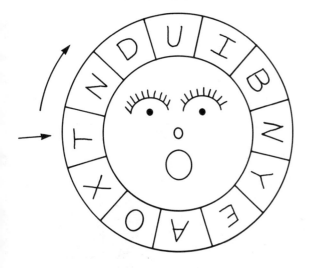

Answer: _____   Answer: _____

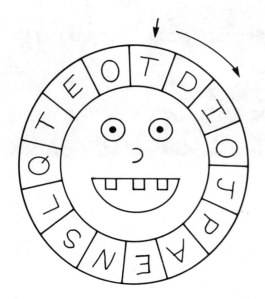

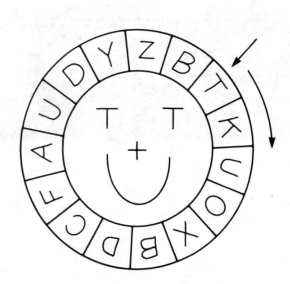

Answer: _____   Answer: _____

WORD CIRCLES

/T/ MEDIAL POSITION

FIND EVERY THIRD LETTER to find out what the puzzle says. Start at the arrow.

_____ Say each word _____ times.
_____ Learn the definition of each word.
_____ Write a sentence for each word.
_____ Make up a story using some of the words from the puzzle.
_____ Draw pictures of some of the words from the puzzle.
_____ Play "I Spy." Look around the classroom and find the words or the objects they represent.

_____ .

Answer: _____

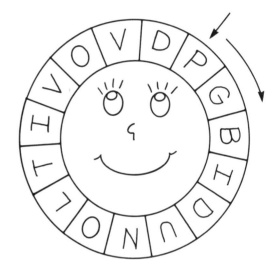

Answer: _____

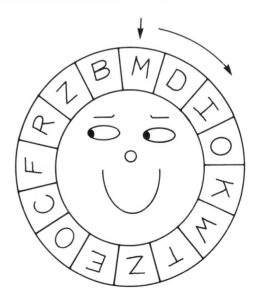

Answer: _____

Answer: _____

WORD CIRCLES

/T/ FINAL POSITION

FIND EVERY THIRD LETTER to find out what the puzzle says. Start at the arrow.

_____ Say each word _____ times.
_____ Learn the definition of each word.
_____ Write a sentence for each word.
_____ Make up a story using some of the words from the puzzle.
_____ Draw pictures of some of the words from the puzzle.
_____ Play "I Spy." Look around the classroom and find the words or the objects they represent.

_____ _____ .

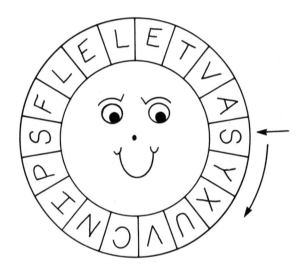

Answer: _____

Answer: _____

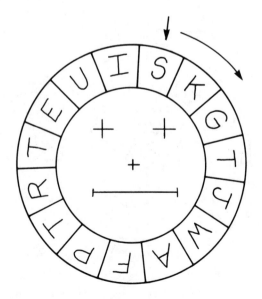

Answer: _____

Answer: _____

Name _____ Date _____

DOTTED WORDS

/T/ INITIAL POSITION

COLOR THE DOTTED LETTERS to find the words.

_____ Say each word _____ times.
_____ Learn the definition of each word.
_____ Write a sentence for each word.
_____ Make up a story using one or both of the words from the puzzle.
_____ Draw pictures of one or both of the words from the puzzle.
_____ Play "I Spy." Look around the classroom and find the words or the objects they
       represent.

_____ _____ .

ANSWERS: _____   _____

Name _____ Date _____

DOTTED WORDS

/T/ MEDIAL POSITION

COLOR THE DOTTED LETTERS to find the words.

_____ Say each word _____ times.
_____ Learn the definition of each word.
_____ Write a sentence for each word.
_____ Make up a story using one or both of the words from the puzzle.
_____ Draw pictures of one or both of the words from the puzzle.
_____ Play "I Spy." Look around the classroom and find the words or the objects they represent.

_____ _____ .

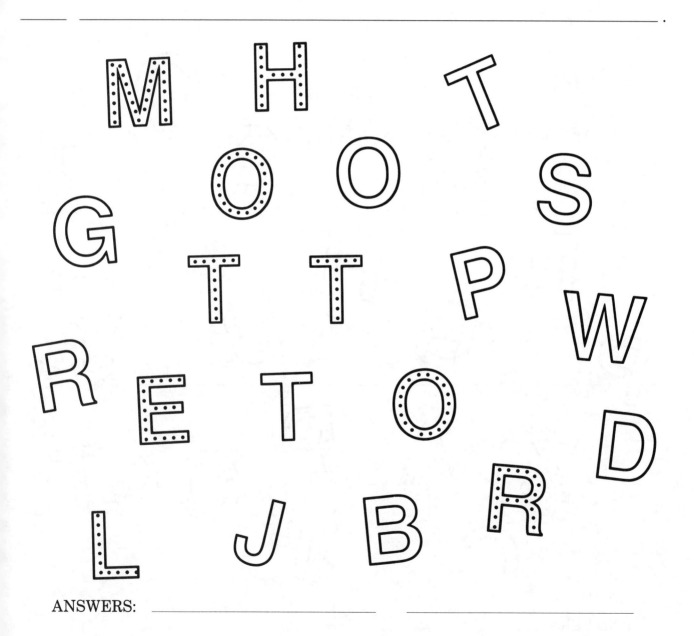

ANSWERS: _____   _____

Name _____   Date _____

DOTTED WORDS

/T/ FINAL POSITION

COLOR THE DOTTED LETTERS to find the words.

_____ Say each word _____ times.
_____ Learn the definition of each word.
_____ Write a sentence for each word.
_____ Make up a story using one or both of the words from the puzzle.
_____ Draw pictures of one or both of the words from the puzzle.
_____ Play "I Spy." Look around the classroom and find the words or the objects they
represent.

_____ _____ .

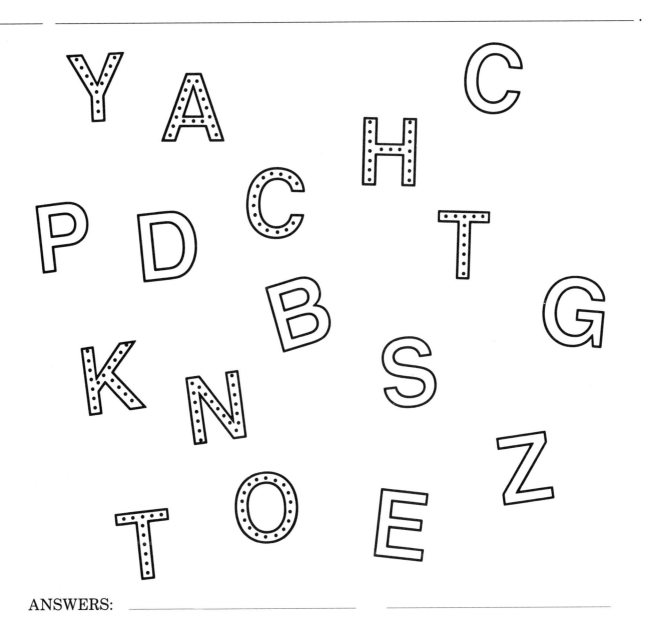

ANSWERS: _____   _____

SECRET CODES

/T/ INITIAL POSITION

USE THE SECRET CODE TO SOLVE THE CODED WORDS. The answers are found at the bottom of this page in the Word Box.

_____ Say each word _____ times.
_____ Learn the definition of each word.
_____ Write a sentence for each word.
_____ Make up a story using some of the words from the puzzle.
_____ Draw pictures of some of the words from the puzzle.
_____ Play "I Spy." Look around the classroom and find the words or the objects they represent.

_____ _____ .

•SECRET CODE•										
A	**B**	**C**	**D**	**E**	**F**	**G**	**H**	**I**	**J**	**K**
5	10	15	20	25	30	35	40	45	50	55
L	**M**	**N**	**O**	**P**	**Q**	**R**	**S**	**T**	**U**	**V**
60	65	70	75	80	85	90	95	100	105	110
W	**X**	**Y**	**Z**							
115	120	125	130							

1. 100 25 70 20 25 90
   __ __ __ __ __ __

2. 100 25 70
   __ __ __

3. 100 25 60 60
   __ __ __ __

4. 100 75 70 35 105 25
   __ __ __ __ __ __

5. 100 75 20 5 125
   __ __ __ __ __

6. 100 75 35 25 100 40 25 90
   __ __ __ __ __ __ __ __

7. 100 105 60 45 80 95
   __ __ __ __ __ __

8. 100 75 115 25 60
   __ __ __ __ __

9. 100 105 90 100 60 25
   __ __ __ __ __ __

10. 100 110
    __ __

•WORD BOX•				
TELL	TENDER	TOGETHER	TOWEL	TURTLE
TEN	TODAY	TONGUE	TULIPS	TV

SECRET CODES

/T/ MEDIAL POSITION

USE THE SECRET CODE TO SOLVE THE CODED WORDS. The answers are found at the bottom of this page in the Word Box.

_____ Say each word _____ times.
_____ Learn the definition of each word.
_____ Write a sentence for each word.
_____ Make up a story using some of the words from the puzzle.
_____ Draw pictures of some of the words from the puzzle.
_____ Play "I Spy." Look around the classroom and find the words or the objects they represent.

_____ _____ .

•SECRET CODE•										
A	**B**	**C**	**D**	**E**	**F**	**G**	**H**	**I**	**J**	**K**
5	10	15	20	25	30	35	40	45	50	55
L	**M**	**N**	**O**	**P**	**Q**	**R**	**S**	**T**	**U**	**V**
60	65	70	75	80	85	90	95	100	105	110
W	**X**	**Y**	**Z**							
115	120	125	130							

1. 5 100 100 45 15

    ___ ___ ___ ___ ___

2. 40 75 100 25 60

    ___ ___ ___ ___ ___

3. 25 5 100 45 70 35

    ___ ___ ___ ___ ___ ___

4. 10 25 100 100 25 90

    ___ ___ ___ ___ ___ ___

5. 20 105 100 45 25 95

    ___ ___ ___ ___ ___ ___

6. 15 75 65 80 105 100 25 90

    ___ ___ ___ ___ ___ ___ ___ ___

7. 80 75 100 5 100 75

    ___ ___ ___ ___ ___ ___

8. 110 45 100 5 65 45 70 95

    ___ ___ ___ ___ ___ ___ ___ ___

9. 55 45 100 100 25 70

    ___ ___ ___ ___ ___ ___

10. 85 105 45 100 100 25 90

    ___ ___ ___ ___ ___ ___ ___

•WORD BOX•				
ATTIC	COMPUTER	EATING	KITTEN	QUITTER
BETTER	DUTIES	HOTEL	POTATO	VITAMINS

Name _____   Date _____

SECRET CODES

/T/ FINAL POSITION

USE THE SECRET CODE TO SOLVE THE CODED WORDS. The answers are found at the bottom of this page in the Word Box.

_____ Say each word _____ times.
_____ Learn the definition of each word.
_____ Write a sentence for each word.
_____ Make up a story using some of the words from the puzzle.
_____ Draw pictures of some of the words from the puzzle.
_____ Play "I Spy." Look around the classroom and find the words or the objects they represent.

_____ _____ .

•SECRET CODE•										
A	B	C	D	E	F	G	H	I	J	K
5	10	15	20	25	30	35	40	45	50	55
L	M	N	O	P	Q	R	S	T	U	V
60	65	70	75	80	85	90	95	100	105	110
W	X	Y	Z							
115	120	125	130							

1. 50 25 100
    __ __ __

2. 35 5 100 25
    __ __ __ __

3. 30 90 105 45 100
    __ __ __ __ __

4. 5 10 75 105 100
    __ __ __ __ __

5. 95 100 5 100 25
    __ __ __ __ __

6. 75 80 25 90 5 100 25
    __ __ __ __ __ __ __

7. 55 70 75 100
    __ __ __ __

8. 95 55 5 100 25
    __ __ __ __ __

9. 115 5 60 60 25 100
    __ __ __ __ __ __

10. 105 70 30 45 100
     __ __ __ __ __

•WORD BOX•				
ABOUT	GATE	KNOT	SKATE	UNFIT
FRUIT	JET	OPERATE	STATE	WALLET

SCRAMBLED WORDS

/T/ INITIAL POSITION

UNSCRAMBLE THE WORDS. The answers are in the Word Box.

_____ Say each word _____ times.
_____ Learn the definition of each word.
_____ Write a sentence for each word.
_____ Make up a story using some of the words from the puzzle.
_____ Draw pictures of some of the words from the puzzle.
_____ Play "I Spy." Look around the classroom and find the words or the objects they represent.

_____ _____ .

1. OLOST   _____

2. AESTT   _____

3. ALTOT   _____

4. LETESIVION   _____

5. AMOOTT   _____

6. LTKA   _____

7. ETEANRGE   _____

8. BEATL   _____

9. TEHET   _____

10. ETKA   _____

11. XBTACIA   _____

12. RLTUTE   _____

13. DERTI   _____

14. OOOLTXB   _____

15. OCAT   _____

```
•WORD BOX•
TABLE      TALK       TELEVISION     TIRED       TOOLS
TACO       TASTE      TEENAGER       TOMATO      TOTAL
TAKE       TAXICAB    TEETH          TOOLBOX     TURTLE
```

Name _____ Date _____

SCRAMBLED WORDS

/T/ MEDIAL POSITION

UNSCRAMBLE THE WORDS. The answers are in the Word Box.

_____ Say each word _____ times.
_____ Learn the definition of each word.
_____ Write a sentence for each word.
_____ Make up a story using some of the words from the puzzle.
_____ Draw pictures of some of the words from the puzzle.
_____ Play "I Spy." Look around the classroom and find the words or the objects they
       represent.

_____ _____ .

1. YITC   _____

2. EAREHT   _____

3. NBUOTT   _____

4. NOOTTC   _____

5. ATBEUY   _____

6. OEDACLT   _____

7. IRWTRE   _____

8. VELETARO   _____

9. RETAW   _____

10. VRIOSTI   _____

11. RTOGNOEFT   _____

12. TOTOPA   _____

13. HEATTER   _____

14. ROPERATO   _____

15. HOSTILPA   _____

•WORD BOX•

BEAUTY	COTTON	HEATER	OPERATOR	VISITOR
BUTTON	ELEVATOR	HOSPITAL	POTATO	WATER
CITY	FORGOTTEN	LOCATED	THEATER	WRITER

Name _____ Date _____

SCRAMBLED WORDS

/T/ FINAL POSITION

UNSCRAMBLE THE WORDS. The answers are in the Word Box.

_____ Say each word _____ times.
_____ Learn the definition of each word.
_____ Write a sentence for each word.
_____ Make up a story using some of the words from the puzzle.
_____ Draw pictures of some of the words from the puzzle.
_____ Play "I Spy." Look around the classroom and find the words or the objects they represent.

_____.

1. TEW   _____

2. OCTA   _____

3. KPOTCE   _____

4. BTAO   _____

5. EUPTS   _____

6. TKECJA   _____

7. TAC   _____

8. TEG   _____

9. ETA   _____

10. OORFGT   _____

11. LAPET   _____

12. RLCANTEI   _____

13. LOTIEV   _____

14. MARKETSUPER   _____

15. NUTCOOC   _____

•WORD BOX•				
ATE	CLARINET	FORGOT	PLATE	UPSET
BOAT	COAT	GET	POCKET	VIOLET
CAT	COCONUT	JACKET	SUPERMARKET	WET

WORD FIND

/T/ INITIAL POSITION

FIND THE WORDS IN THE WORD BOX THAT ARE HIDDEN IN THE PUZZLE. They may be hidden down, across, upside down, diagonal, or backwards.

_____ Say each word _____ times.
_____ Learn the definition of each word.
_____ Write a sentence for each word.
_____ Make up a story using some of the words from the puzzle.
_____ Draw pictures of some of the words from the puzzle.
_____ Play "I Spy." Look around the classroom and find the words or the objects they represent.

_____ _____ .

```
T  A  H  T  B  G  P  Z  T  C  I  N  T
S  T  O  O  T  H  B  R  U  S  H  I  Z
E  E  Z  N  Q  F  Y  E  T  F  A  P  V
L  R  X  Y  J  D  T  X  O  R  D  S  A
A  R  C  T  A  X  I  B  R  J  Y  L  M
M  A  T  W  O  I  G  T  W  F  E  I  Q
A  C  H  K  G  V  H  T  M  S  X  A  L
T  E  D  D  Y  S  T  A  U  G  H  T  P
A  P  U  Q  O  Y  E  U  V  T  F  A  R
N  T  L  N  P  T  M  D  I  O  L  V  X
K  R  U  I  N  K  P  T  T  O  X  Z
E  L  C  M  T  I  E  J  Y  L  I  N  Y
R  A  K  Q  F  C  R  D  L  T  M  O  B
L  F  B  T  A  X  E  S  Z  T  L  T  N
```

•WORD BOX•		
TAILSPIN	TEAM	TON
TAMALES	TEDDY	TOOTHBRUSH
TANKER	TEMPER	TUITION
TAUGHT	TERRACE	TUTOR
TAXES	TIE	TYPICAL
TAXI	TIGHT	

Name _____ Date _____

WORD FIND

/T/ MEDIAL POSITION

FIND THE WORDS IN THE WORD BOX THAT ARE HIDDEN IN THE PUZZLE. They
may be hidden down, across, upside down, diagonal, or backwards.

_____ Say each word _____ times.
_____ Learn the definition of each word.
_____ Write a sentence for each word.
_____ Make up a story using some of the words from the puzzle.
_____ Draw pictures of some of the words from the puzzle.
_____ Play "I Spy." Look around the classroom and find the words or the objects they
represent.

_____ _____ .

```
P  Z  A  T  G  K  J  F  A  T  T  E  R  A
Q  X  T  G  U  L  S  T  D  I  T  T  Y  D
A  A  T  K  I  T  R  B  A  I  T  E  D  N
D  F  E  B  T  V  E  L  Y  G  S  F  T  E
Z  R  N  I  A  J  T  D  N  T  A  R  N  T
X  E  D  C  R  U  T  E  A  W  E  E  R  T
B  T  M  E  H  R  I  T  T  Q  Z  T  E  O
F  E  H  L  Y  T  J  O  O  T  D  E  T  G
L  I  T  T  E  R  P  U  B  K  X  M  A  R
H  U  I  I  O  O  G  R  J  T  M  F  R  O
T  Q  N  T  L  R  O  T  A  N  E  S  C  F
```

•WORD BOX•		
ATTEND	DITTY	LITTER
BAITED	FATTER	METER
BOTANY	FORGOTTEN	QUIETER
CRATER	GUITAR	SENATOR
DETOUR	JITTERS	TITLE

WORD FIND

/J/ FINAL POSITION

FIND THE WORDS IN THE WORD BOX THAT ARE HIDDEN IN THE PUZZLE. They
may be hidden down, across, upside down, diagonal, or backwards.

_____ Say each word _____ times.
_____ Learn the definition of each word.
_____ Write a sentence for each word.
_____ Make up a story using some of the words from the puzzle.
_____ Draw pictures of some of the words from the puzzle.
_____ Play "I Spy." Look around the classroom and find the words or the objects they
represent.

_____ _____ .

```
A  F  T  K  D  T  E  K  C  O  P  T  G  K
H  E  I  G  H  T  L  T  C  F  H  F  Y  E
T  H  L  T  E  O  P  E  H  M  B  A  I  T
Q  A  T  E  T  C  T  K  E  T  H  L  I  A
E  V  J  E  L  Z  I  E  A  Z  T  X  Q  C
T  T  B  T  T  O  T  B  T  N  E  M  O
U  E  T  P  H  A  V  K  D  R  C  J  Y  L
R  S  J  I  C  Y  T  Q  D  M  U  R  Q  T
B  P  T  Z  K  L  A  K  O  T  A  C  P  S
T  U  D  E  T  U  N  I  M  Z  F  T  S  T
K  E  L  K  N  O  T  M  W  I  Q  F  T  D
E  T  A  T  I  M  I  E  T  A  C  U  D  E
```

•WORD BOX•

ATE	EXIT	LOCATE
BAIT	FAUCET	MINUTE
BRUTE	HEIGHT	POCKET
CHEAT	IMITATE	POET
EDUCATE	KNOT	UPSET

Name _____ Date _____

CROSSWORD PUZZLE

/T/ INITIAL POSITION

COMPLETE THE PUZZLE. The answers are in the Word Box.

_____ Say each word _____ times.
_____ Learn the definition of each word.
_____ Write a sentence for each word.
_____ Make up a story using some of the words from the puzzle.
_____ Draw pictures of some of the words from the puzzle.
_____ Play "I Spy." Look around the classroom and find the words or the objects they represent.

_____ .

•WORD BOX•

TANTRUM	TEENAGER	TICKLE	TIRED	TRY
TEACHER	TELEVISION	TIME	TOGETHER	TURN
TEAKETTLE	TEMPER	TIMID	TRIM	

ACROSS
3. To attempt
4. "Idiot Box"
5. Amuse
6. Used to boil water
9. Angry outburst
10. Mood

DOWN
1. A person between the ages of 13 and 19
2. Shy
3. Fatigued
4. One who teaches
5. Term
7. Jointly
8. Pivot
9. To cut

CROSSWORD PUZZLE

/T/ MEDIAL POSITION

COMPLETE THE PUZZLE. The answers are in the Word Box.

_____ Say each word _____ times.
_____ Learn the definition of each word.
_____ Write a sentence for each word.
_____ Make up a story using some of the words from the puzzle.
_____ Draw pictures of some of the words from the puzzle.
_____ Play "I Spy." Look around the classroom and find the words or the objects they represent.

_____ _____ .

•WORD BOX•

BATTER	LETTUCE	NAUGHTY	PRETTY	TOTAL
CITY	MITTENS	PHOTOGRAPH	RATTLE	TUTOR
DATA	MOTOR	POTATO	TOMATO	WATER
GUITAR				

ACROSS
3. Pleasant to look at
5. Information
6. Spud
7. Teacher
8. Salad basis
11. Gloves
14. Musical instrument
15. Clear liquid

DOWN
1. Baby's toy
2. One who hits the ball
3. Picture
4. All
9. Red, acidic vegetable
10. Town
12. Misbehave
13. Engine

CROSSWORD PUZZLE

/T/ FINAL POSITION

COMPLETE THE PUZZLE. The answers are in the Word Box.

_____ Say each word _____ times.
_____ Learn the definition of each word.
_____ Write a sentence for each word.
_____ Make up a story using some of the words from the puzzle.
_____ Draw pictures of some of the words from the puzzle.
_____ Play "I Spy." Look around the classroom and find the words or the objects they represent.

_____ _____ .

•WORD BOX•

ATE	CREATE	IT	OPERATE	SPOT
CHOCOLATE	EAT	LIGHT	SEAT	SUIT
COAT	GOAT	MEET	SHUT	THOUGHT
COMPLIMENT				

ACROSS
1. Delicious candy
5. An idea
7. Warm clothing
8. Past tense of eat
10. Men's clothing
12. To close

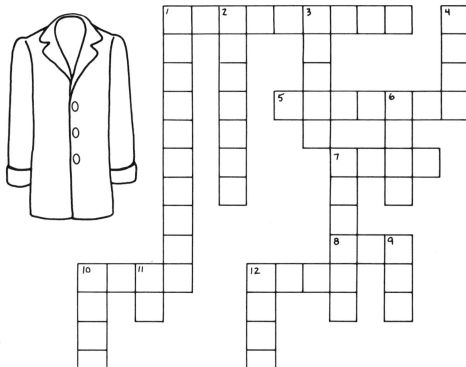

DOWN
1. To praise
2. To perform surgery
3. Weightless
4. To assemble
6. Animal that will eat anything
7. To make
9. To consume food
10. A chair
11. Object
12. A smudge

ACTIVITIES FOR / V /

WORD CIRCLES

/V/ INITIAL POSITION

FIND EVERY THIRD LETTER to find out what the puzzle says. Start at the arrow.

_____ Say each word _____ times.
_____ Learn the definition of each word.
_____ Write a sentence for each word.
_____ Make up a story using some of the words from the puzzle.
_____ Draw pictures of some of the words from the puzzle.
_____ Play "I Spy." Look around the classroom and find the words or the objects they
represent.

_____ _____.

Answer: _____   Answer: _____

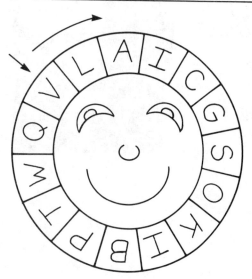

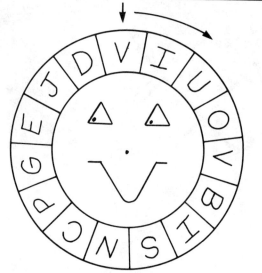

Answer: _____   Answer: _____

Name _____ Date _____

WORD CIRCLES

/V/ MEDIAL POSITION

FIND EVERY THIRD LETTER to find out what the puzzle says. Start at the arrow.

_____ Say each word _____ times.
_____ Learn the definition of each word.
_____ Write a sentence for each word.
_____ Make up a story using some of the words from the puzzle.
_____ Draw pictures of some of the words from the puzzle.
_____ Play "I Spy." Look around the classroom and find the words or the objects they represent.

_____ _____ .

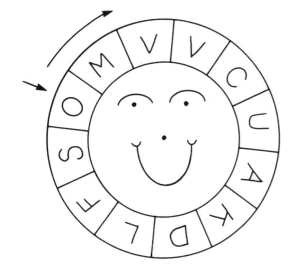

Answer: _____

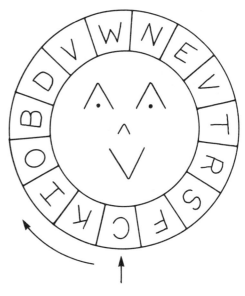

Answer: _____

Answer: _____

Answer: _____

WORD CIRCLES

/V/ FINAL POSITION

FIND EVERY THIRD LETTER to find out what the puzzle says. Start at the arrow.

_____ Say each word _____ times.
_____ Learn the definition of each word.
_____ Write a sentence for each word.
_____ Make up a story using some of the words from the puzzle.
_____ Draw pictures of some of the words from the puzzle.
_____ Play "I Spy." Look around the classroom and find the words or the objects they
        represent.

_____ _____ .

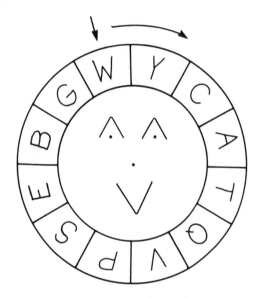

Answer: _____   Answer: _____

Answer: _____   Answer: _____

Name _____ Date _____

DOTTED WORDS

/V/ INITIAL POSITION

COLOR THE DOTTED LETTERS to find the words.

_____ Say each word _____ times.
_____ Learn the definition of each word.
_____ Write a sentence for each word.
_____ Make up a story using one or both of the words from the puzzle.
_____ Draw pictures of one or both of the words from the puzzle.
_____ Play "I Spy." Look around the classroom and find the words or the objects they represent.

_____ _____ .

ANSWERS: _____ _____

DOTTED WORDS

/V/ MEDIAL POSITION

COLOR THE DOTTED LETTERS to find the words.

_____ Say each word _____ times.
_____ Learn the definition of each word.
_____ Write a sentence for each word.
_____ Make up a story using one or both of the words from the puzzle.
_____ Draw pictures of one or both of the words from the puzzle.
_____ Play "I Spy." Look around the classroom and find the words or the objects they represent.

_____ _____ .

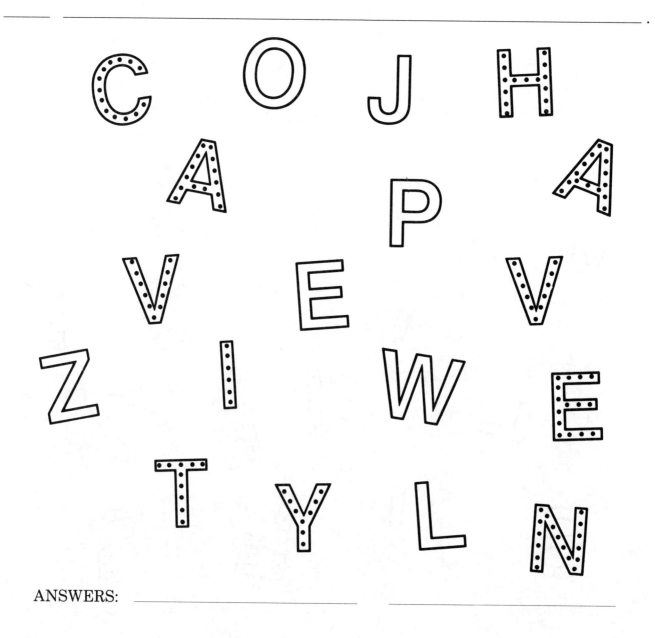

ANSWERS: _____   _____

Name _____   Date _____

DOTTED WORDS

/V/ FINAL POSITION

COLOR THE DOTTED LETTERS to find the words.

_____ Say each word _____ times.
_____ Learn the definition of each word.
_____ Write a sentence for each word.
_____ Make up a story using one or both of the words from the puzzle.
_____ Draw pictures of one or both of the words from the puzzle.
_____ Play "I Spy." Look around the classroom and find the words or the objects they represent.

_____ _____ .

ANSWERS: _____   _____

SECRET CODES

/V/ INITIAL POSITION

USE THE SECRET CODE TO SOLVE THE CODED WORDS. The answers are found at the bottom of this page in the Word Box.

_____ Say each word _____ times.
_____ Learn the definition of each word.
_____ Write a sentence for each word.
_____ Make up a story using some of the words from the puzzle.
_____ Draw pictures of some of the words from the puzzle.
_____ Play "I Spy." Look around the classroom and find the words or the objects they represent.

_____ _____ .

•SECRET CODE•										
A	**B**	**C**	**D**	**E**	**F**	**G**	**H**	**I**	**J**	**K**
1	2	3	4	5	6	7	8	9	10	11
L	**M**	**N**	**O**	**P**	**Q**	**R**	**S**	**T**	**U**	**V**
12	13	14	15	16	17	18	19	20	21	22
W	**X**	**Y**	**Z**							
23	24	25	26							

1. 22 15 20 5
   __ __ __ __

2. 22 1 12 12 5 25
   __ __ __ __ __ __

3. 22 1 12 9 4
   __ __ __ __ __

4. 22 9 14 5 19
   __ __ __ __ __

5. 22 9 19 9 2 12 5
   __ __ __ __ __ __ __

6. 22 9 12 12 1 7 5
   __ __ __ __ __ __ __

7. 22 9 18 21 19
   __ __ __ __ __

8. 22 5 18 9 6 25
   __ __ __ __ __ __

9. 22 9 19 9 20
   __ __ __ __ __

10. 22 5 18 2 1 12
    __ __ __ __ __ __

•WORD BOX•				
VALID	VERBAL	VILLAGE	VIRUS	VISIT
VALLEY	VERIFY	VINES	VISIBLE	VOTE

SECRET CODES

/V/ MEDIAL POSITION

USE THE SECRET CODE TO SOLVE THE CODED WORDS. The answers are found at the bottom of this page in the Word Box.

_____ Say each word _____ times.
_____ Learn the definition of each word.
_____ Write a sentence for each word.
_____ Make up a story using some of the words from the puzzle.
_____ Draw pictures of some of the words from the puzzle.
_____ Play "I Spy." Look around the classroom and find the words or the objects they
        represent.

_____ _____ .

```
•SECRET CODE•
A    B    C    D    E    F    G    H    I    J    K
1    2    3    4    5    6    7    8    9    10   11
L    M    N    O    P    Q    R    S    T    U    V
12   13   14   15   16   17   18   19   20   21   22
W    X    Y    Z
23   24   25   26
```

1. 1 4 22 5 18 2

    __ __ __ __ __ __

2. 7 18 1 22 25

    __ __ __ __ __

3. 3 15 22 5 18

    __ __ __ __ __

4. 5 22 5 18

    __ __ __ __

5. 5 22 5 14 20

    __ __ __ __ __

6. 8 1 22 9 14 7

    __ __ __ __ __ __

7. 6 12 1 22 15 18

    __ __ __ __ __ __

8. 15 22 5 18 1 12 12 19

    __ __ __ __ __ __ __ __

9. 16 15 22 5 18 20 25

    __ __ __ __ __ __ __

10. 19 5 22 5 14 20 25

    __ __ __ __ __ __ __

```
•WORD BOX•
ADVERB        EVENT       FLAVOR      HAVING        POVERTY
COVER         EVER        GRAVY       OVERALLS      SEVENTY
```

SECRET CODES

/V/ FINAL POSITION

USE THE SECRET CODE TO SOLVE THE CODED WORDS. The answers are found at the bottom of this page in the Word Box.

_____ Say each word _____ times.
_____ Learn the definition of each word.
_____ Write a sentence for each word.
_____ Make up a story using some of the words from the puzzle.
_____ Draw pictures of some of the words from the puzzle.
_____ Play "I Spy." Look around the classroom and find the words or the objects they represent.

_____ _____ .

```
•SECRET CODE•
A    B    C    D    E    F    G    H    I    J    K
1    2    3    4    5    6    7    8    9    10   11
L    M    N    O    P    Q    R    S    T    U    V
12   13   14   15   16   17   18   19   20   21   22
W    X    Y    Z
23   24   25   26
```

1. 12 5   1   22 5
    __ __ __ __ __

2. 23 5   22 5
    __ __ __ __

3. 16 18 15 22 5
    __ __ __ __ __

4. 19 12 5   5   22 5
    __ __ __ __ __ __

5. 18 5   20 18 9   5   22 5
    __ __ __ __ __ __ __ __

6. 3   1   22 5
    __ __ __ __

7. 6   9   22 5
    __ __ __ __

8. 6   15 18 7   9   22 5
    __ __ __ __ __ __ __

9. 15 12 9   22 5
    __ __ __ __ __

10. 1   18 18 9   22 5
    __ __ __ __ __ __

```
•WORD BOX•
ARRIVE        FIVE          LEAVE         PROVE         SLEEVE
CAVE          FORGIVE       OLIVE         RETRIEVE      WE'VE
```

SCRAMBLED WORDS

/V/ INITIAL POSITION

UNSCRAMBLE THE WORDS. The answers are in the Word Box.

_____ Say each word _____ times.
_____ Learn the definition of each word.
_____ Write a sentence for each word.
_____ Make up a story using some of the words from the puzzle.
_____ Draw pictures of some of the words from the puzzle.
_____ Play "I Spy." Look around the classroom and find the words or the objects they represent.

_____ _____ .

1. EOVT   _____

2. LAINLVI   _____

3. VOTICRY   _____

4. VONLCAO   _____

5. VNOITACA   _____

6. VTELOI   _____

7. VBRE   _____

8. VNA   _____

9. WVLEO   _____

10. ECIOV   _____

11. LGIVEAL   _____

12. OEVIL   _____

13. VVEETL   _____

14. TENSV   _____

15. IVINSO   _____

•WORD BOX•

VACATION	VENTS	VICTORY	VIOLET	VOILE
VAN	VERB	VILLAGE	VISION	VOLCANO
VELVET	VETO	VILLAIN	VOICE	VOWEL

SCRAMBLED WORDS

/V/ MEDIAL POSITION

UNSCRAMBLE THE WORDS. The answers are in the Word Box.

_____ Say each word _____ times.
_____ Learn the definition of each word.
_____ Write a sentence for each word.
_____ Make up a story using some of the words from the puzzle.
_____ Draw pictures of some of the words from the puzzle.
_____ Play "I Spy." Look around the classroom and find the words or the objects they represent.

_____ _____ .

1. LEREVC   _____

2. TMIERVEO   _____

3. YEVYEBDOR   _____

4. BEVERA   _____

5. NEVE   _____

6. REVEFOR   _____

7. DOTEVE   _____

8. DEVIRR   _____

9. DEPOLEV   _____

10. REVFE   _____

11. VLENEE   _____

12. ENEVS   _____

13. AVENHE   _____

14. NEOV   _____

15. ELEIVRD   _____

•WORD BOX•				
BEAVER	DEVELOP	ELEVEN	FEVER	OVEN
CLEVER	DEVOTE	EVEN	FOREVER	OVERTIME
DELIVER	DRIVER	EVERYBODY	HEAVEN	SEVEN

SCRAMBLED WORDS

/V/ FINAL POSITION

UNSCRAMBLE THE WORDS. The answers are in the Word Box.

_____ Say each word _____ times.
_____ Learn the definition of each word.
_____ Write a sentence for each word.
_____ Make up a story using some of the words from the puzzle.
_____ Draw pictures of some of the words from the puzzle.
_____ Play "I Spy." Look around the classroom and find the words or the objects they represent.

_____ _____ .

1. LEREIEV   _____
2. EVAG   _____
3. RIMPVEO   _____
4. VABOE   _____
5. BEVELEI   _____
6. RDVEI   _____
7. LAVIETER   _____
8. VERBA   _____
9. EVERMO   _____
10. EVAH   _____
11. VSEAH   _____
12. EVTOS   _____
13. ELOV   _____
14. PSEEVEINX   _____
15. VRAREI   _____

•WORD BOX•

ABOVE	BRAVE	GAVE	LOVE	REMOVE
ARRIVE	DRIVE	HAVE	RELATIVE	SHAVE
BELIEVE	EXPENSIVE	IMPROVE	RELIEVE	STOVE

Name _____   Date _____

WORD FIND

/V/ INITIAL POSITION

FIND THE WORDS IN THE WORD BOX THAT ARE HIDDEN IN THE PUZZLE. They may be hidden down, across, upside down, diagonal, or backwards.

_____ Say each word _____ times.
_____ Learn the definition of each word.
_____ Write a sentence for each word.
_____ Make up a story using some of the words from the puzzle.
_____ Draw pictures of some of the words from the puzzle.
_____ Play "I Spy." Look around the classroom and find the words or the objects they represent.

_____ _____ .

```
D  N  V  O  N  A  R  E  T  E  V  P  B
F  E  U  G  A  V  M  V  G  I  I  V  R
P  V  H  V  A  I  N  W  C  J  C  O  V
J  O  V  A  L  I  D  H  K  Q  T  I  E
V  W  B  H  V  R  Y  C  E  Z  O  C  L
I  E  O  V  N  S  A  S  Y  L  R  E  B
N  L  U  W  S  V  R  F  S  D  Y  S  I
T  V  P  O  C  E  I  E  Y  V  M  Q  S
A  K  I  T  V  R  V  A  L  I  S  E  I
G  S  F  T  E  X  T  E  L  O  I  V  V
E  L  D  V  A  L  I  A  N  T  V  A  V
```

•WORD BOX•		
VAGUE	VERIFY	VINTAGE
VAIN	VERSE	VIOLET
VALIANT	VETERAN	VISIBLE
VALID	VICHYSSOISE	VOICE
VALISE	VICTORY	VOWEL

WORD FIND

/V/ MEDIAL POSITION

FIND THE WORDS IN THE WORD BOX THAT ARE HIDDEN IN THE PUZZLE. They may be hidden down, across, upside down, diagonal, or backwards.

_____ Say each word _____ times.
_____ Learn the definition of each word.
_____ Write a sentence for each word.
_____ Make up a story using some of the words from the puzzle.
_____ Draw pictures of some of the words from the puzzle.
_____ Play "I Spy." Look around the classroom and find the words or the objects they represent.

_____ _____ .

```
Z  G  Z  G  R  A  V  E  L  Z  N  G
I  H  O  V  E  L  V  N  G  M  R  G
M  A  D  G  Y  L  H  E  A  V  E  N
Y  D  H  K  O  J  H  A  V  O  C  P
F  V  Y  V  B  X  G  A  E  Q  S  T
J  E  E  L  L  P  M  V  R  O  Z  A
D  R  K  C  I  V  Y  O  S  V  G  V
K  T  A  G  V  D  G  W  E  E  T  A
B  I  G  F  E  V  E  R  V  R  T  R
Z  S  M  W  R  L  E  G  G  G  G  C
A  E  G  O  V  E  R  N  E  S  S  U
H  I  Z  M  L  E  V  I  R  D  G  F
A  L  M  I  V  E  Z  O  U  I  M  D
```

•WORD BOX•		
ADVERTISE	FEVER	HOVEL
AVERSE	GOVERNESS	LIVER
AVOW	GRAVEL	IVY
CRAVAT	HAVOC	OVER
DRIVEL	HEAVEN	REVOLVE

WORD FIND

/V/ FINAL POSITION

FIND THE WORDS IN THE WORD BOX THAT ARE HIDDEN IN THE PUZZLE. They may be hidden down, across, upside down, diagonal, or backwards.

_____ Say each word _____ times.
_____ Learn the definition of each word.
_____ Write a sentence for each word.
_____ Make up a story using some of the words from the puzzle.
_____ Draw pictures of some of the words from the puzzle.
_____ Play "I Spy." Look around the classroom and find the words or the objects they represent.

_____ _____ .

```
E  E  V  E  V  A  C  X  N  M  Z  V
V  V  Y  T  N  B  C  V  T  O  L  E
A  L  I  V  E  A  Z  O  U  T  V  A
H  C  F  J  H  N  R  P  V  I  E  Z
E  M  O  X  B  V  L  R  Z  V  Z  H
B  I  R  E  L  A  T  I  V  E  X  T
S  L  V  E  R  V  I  M  T  P  N  X
I  O  P  R  I  M  I  T  I  V  E  E
M  A  I  K  E  T  N  T  O  Q  Q  V
B  R  G  L  F  H  O  I  J  P  R  A
E  R  V  N  O  L  I  V  E  K  A  R
V  I  J  C  E  V  T  E  L  L  V  B
V  V  N  V  M  D  E  K  S  C  H  M
K  E  I  T  G  L  O  V  E  U  I  V
P  R  W  I  M  P  R  O  V  E  O  L
D  U  N  L  Z  E  V  I  G  R  O  F
```

•WORD BOX•				
ALIVE	CAVE	GLOVE	MISBEHAVE	OLIVE
ARRIVE	DRIVE	IMPROVE	MOTIVE	PRIMITIVE
BRAVE	FORGIVE	LOVE	MOVE	RELATIVE

CROSSWORD PUZZLE

/V/ INITIAL POSITION

COMPLETE THE PUZZLE. The answers are in the Word Box.

_____ Say each word _____ times.
_____ Learn the definition of each word.
_____ Write a sentence for each word.
_____ Make up a story using some of the words from the puzzle.
_____ Draw pictures of some of the words from the puzzle.
_____ Play "I Spy." Look around the classroom and find the words or the objects they represent.

_____ _____ .

•WORD BOX•

VACANT	VANILLA	VERSION	VICARAGE	VIPER
VALLEY	VAPOR	VERTIGO	VIOLIN	VOWEL
VAN	VERBAL			

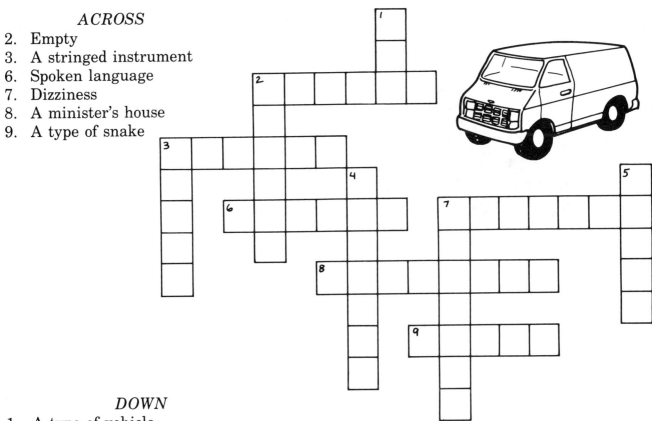

ACROSS
2. Empty
3. A stringed instrument
6. Spoken language
7. Dizziness
8. A minister's house
9. A type of snake

DOWN
1. A type of vehicle
2. Low place between mountains
3. A gaseous form
4. A flavor
5. A, E, I, O, or U
7. A different point of view

CROSSWORD PUZZLE

/V/ MEDIAL POSITION

COMPLETE THE PUZZLE. The answers are in the Word Box.

_____ Say each word _____ times.
_____ Learn the definition of each word.
_____ Write a sentence for each word.
_____ Make up a story using some of the words from the puzzle.
_____ Draw pictures of some of the words from the puzzle.
_____ Play "I Spy." Look around the classroom and find the words or the objects they
represent.

_____ _____ .

•WORD BOX•				
BEAVER	COVERING	ELEVATOR	NAVY	REVIEW
BRAVERY	DELIVER	LAVA	OVER	SEVENTH

ACROSS
2. Something placed over something else
3. After sixth
5. To display courage
7. Volcanic substance
8. Above
9. A mechanical lift

DOWN
1. To take to
4. U.S. fleet of ships
5. Animal that builds dams
6. To go over

CROSSWORD PUZZLE

/V/ FINAL POSITION

COMPLETE THE PUZZLE. The answers are in the Word Box.

_____ Say each word _____ times.
_____ Learn the definition of each word.
_____ Write a sentence for each word.
_____ Make up a story using some of the words from the puzzle.
_____ Draw pictures of some of the words from the puzzle.
_____ Play "I Spy." Look around the classroom and find the words or the objects they represent.

_____ _____ .

•WORD BOX•

ABOVE	FIVE	GIVE	OLIVE	PRIMITIVE
DIVE	GAVE	LOVE	POSITIVE	THRIVE
EXPENSIVE				

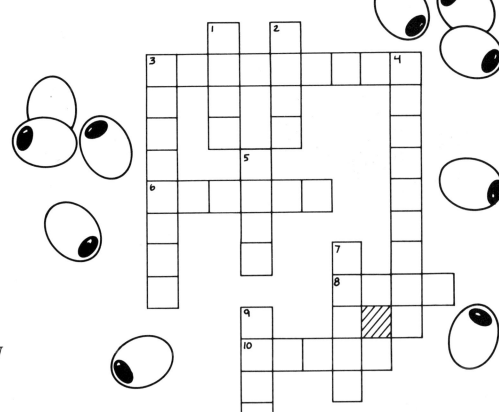

ACROSS
3. Simple
6. To live
8. An emotion
10. Overhead

DOWN
1. A jump
2. To offer
3. Certain
4. Costing too much money
5. Before 6
7. A round, green fruit
9. Past tense of give

ANSWER KEYS

/CH/ ANSWER KEYS

Word Circles: /CH/ Initial Position

chain, child, champ, chow

Word Circles: /CH/ Medial Position

future, inches, nature, statue

Word Circles: /CH/ Final Position

torch, arch, march, porch

Dotted Words: /CH/ Initial Position

charm, cheap

Dotted Words: /CH/ Medial Position

nachos, picture

Dotted Words: /CH/ Final Position

watch, beach

Secret Codes: /CH/ Initial Position

1. chain
2. channel
3. chapter
4. check
5. cheer
6. chunk
7. churn
8. cheap
9. change
10. charity

Secret Codes: /CH/ Medial Position

1. dentures
2. question
3. statue
4. adventure
5. mutual
6. reaching
7. picture
8. culture
9. texture
10. feature

Secret Codes: /CH/ Final Position

1. latch
2. grouch
3. approach
4. wrench
5. stretch
6. attach
7. stitch
8. couch
9. patch
10. ouch

Scrambled Words: /CH/ Initial Position

1. chance
2. choke
3. checkers
4. chin
5. chilly
6. charity
7. chat
8. cheat
9. checkbook
10. chapter
11. chess
12. church
13. cheese
14. cherries
15. chosen

Scrambled Words: /CH/ Medial Position

1. adventure
2. watching
3. kitchen
4. lecture
5. reaching
6. picture
7. armchair
8. furniture
9. beachball
10. creature
11. grandchild
12. peaches
13. future
14. teaching
15. butcher

Scrambled Words: /CH/ Final Position

1. preach
2. attach
3. branch
4. hopscotch
5. fetch
6. scratch
7. touch
8. ditch
9. lunch
10. each
11. bleach
12. catch
13. sandwich
14. ostrich
15. ranch

Word Find: /CH/ Initial Position

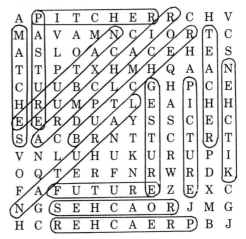

Word Find: /CH/ Medial Position

Word Find: /CH/ Final Position

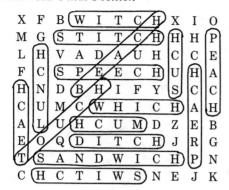

Crossword Puzzle: /CH/ Initial Position

ACROSS	DOWN
1. chairman	1. choose
3. cherry	2. chess
4. chop	5. check
5. checkers	6. chimney
7. cheese	7. children
9. cheap	8. chipmunks
10. chin	9. china

Crossword Puzzle: /CH/ Medial Position

ACROSS	DOWN
1. grandchild	2. amateur
5. etches	3. creature
8. lecture	4. inches
9. gesture	6. satchel
11. armchair	7. beachball
12. witches	10. searching
13. lunchroom	

Crossword Puzzle: /CH/ Final Position

ACROSS	DOWN
1. approach	1. avalanche
5. latch	2. ranch
6. cockroach	3. couch
8. coach	4. each
10. wrench	7. ostrich
11. itch	9. hopscotch
13. watch	12. bench
14. teach	
15. pitch	

/D/ ANSWER KEYS

Word Circles: /D/ Initial Position

dear, deal, defeat, date

Word Circles: /D/ Medial Position

study, idea, under, body

Word Circles: /D/ Final Position

salad, shade, depend, cord

Dotted Words: /D/ Initial Position

dog, day

Dotted Words: /D/ Medial Position

hot dog, lady

Dotted Words: /D/ Final Position

add, wide

Secret Codes: /D/ Initial Position

1. dawn	6. dandruff
2. double	7. dozen
3. defeat	8. dizzy
4. dismiss	9. denial
5. duet	10. dance

Secret Codes: /D/ Medial Position

1. odorous	6. tidy
2. rider	7. vandals
3. rodeo	8. headache
4. medicine	9. hidden
5. medial	10. shudder

Secret Codes: /D/ Final Position

1. lemonade	6. wide
2. aided	7. could
3. spotted	8. tried
4. moved	9. shade
5. needed	10. bread

Scrambled Words: /D/ Initial Position

1. discovery	9. delicate
2. dinosaur	10. day
3. dial	11. decide
4. decent	12. deep
5. dairy	13. democracy
6. dessert	14. diet
7. desert	15. danger
8. different	

Scrambled Words: /D/ Medial Position

1. lady	9. powder
2. odor	10. spider
3. daddy	11. radar
4. feeding	12. chowder
5. medicine	13. birthday
6. today	14. body
7. radio	15. ladder
8. hot dog	

Scrambled Words: /D/ Final Position

1. could	9. bead
2. hide	10. bread
3. lied	11. railroad
4. ad	12. dragged
5. cried	13. salad
6. tide	14. ahead
7. food	15. bed
8. had	

Word Find: /D/ Initial Position

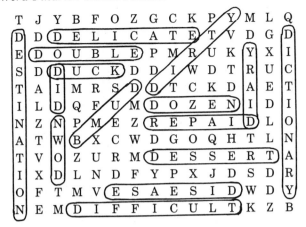

Word Find: /D/ Medial Position

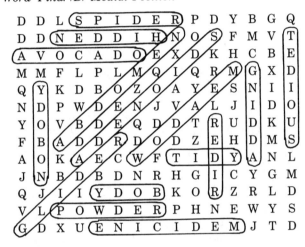

Word Find: /D/ Final Position

Crossword Puzzle: /D/ Initial Position

ACROSS
2. dawn
3. daddy long legs
6. demand
8. danger
9. defective
10. debtor
11. deal

DOWN
1. down
2. doll
3. dandelion
4. diamond
5. deep
7. digest
8. doctor
10. deaf

Crossword Puzzle: /D/ Medial Position

ACROSS
4. spider
5. needle
7. medicine
8. biddy
9. today
10. lady

DOWN
1. ladder
2. birthday
3. kindergarten
6. odor
7. meadow
9. toddler

Crossword Puzzle: /D/ Final Position

ACROSS
1. around
5. cod
6. pretend
7. road
9. red
10. guide
11. wood
12. mad
13. herd
14. rod

DOWN
1. ascend
2. old
3. neighborhood
4. ride
6. persuade
8. dread
12. made

/F/ ANSWER KEYS

Word Circles: /F/ Initial Position

ferry, final, fog, fork

Word Circles: /F/ Medial Position

often, sofa, after, taffy

Word Circles: /F/ Final Position

if, half, stuff, chef

Dotted Words: /F/ Initial Position

face, four

Dotted Words: /F/ Medial Position

coffee, after

Dotted Words: /F/ Final Position

if, off

Secret Codes: /F/ Initial Position

1. fable
2. physical
3. phone
4. found
5. forgot
6. funny
7. fatal
8. fetch
9. phobia
10. fierce

Secret Codes: /F/ Medial Position

1. comfort
2. define
3. buffet
4. effective
5. outfield
6. laughing
7. prefix
8. barefoot
9. safety
10. infant

243

Secret Codes: /F/ Final Position

1. puff
2. enough
3. proof
4. sheriff
5. graph
6. thief
7. deaf
8. chief
9. belief
10. tough

Scrambled Words: /F/ Initial Position

1. fashion
2. forecast
3. photo
4. football
5. foolproof
6. fuss
7. farm
8. fat
9. fight
10. future
11. fun
12. forever
13. fork
14. field
15. first

Scrambled Words: /F/ Medial Position

1. effect
2. cafe
3. useful
4. trophy
5. outfit
6. traffic
7. breakfast
8. golfer
9. enforce
10. delightful
11. sofa
12. officer
13. suffer
14. colorful
15. confuse

Scrambled Words: /F/ Final Position

1. telegraph
2. enough
3. knife
4. giraffe
5. chef
6. tough
7. belief
8. sheriff
9. handkerchief
10. rainproof
11. thief
12. life
13. roof
14. beef
15. laugh

Word Find: /F/ Initial Position

```
M W B Q F I G H T F N D T C
C D Y U D N K F M P F C T X
F I S H A J N B T D R U C A
X V P O F S F A L L Z O F F
A Y E R I F L E R T E H N I
F F V Q N I Z E F O Z L W R
T L I A D N V S Y F U H J E
E T F B V E K R E C A F L M
G F B Q R C U P M I K F B A
R L O O A M F A M I L Y C N
O J E H T G L P F O F Z H L
F N U J A F R I F I F M C D
K K N F F Y L N E Y W C G Z
M C F U N E R A L J V A D T
T A Z T O L M D F A H K Q F
```

Word Find: /F/ Medial Position

```
M L Y O F S T I F L E Y O A F
I N F L A T E A F C J M Y C V
F U N F A I R E D F E U B D L
T P X L F Z C L L D F N K Y Z
E R Z R M P T E R R I F I C
R E N Z L A E P T A N A B F Y
E F B C P F V H V F U S X M L
F S T D F R Y A S F D T O F C
R N M O Q F A N Z A F E A T P
E A C Q I W M T Y I X N Z N T
T R S R L E L M T R O F T E N
N T R S G O L D F I S H N P A
I E T V O R M I N F A N T X B
T C O U T F I T L T O F V C D
```

Word Find: /F/ Final Position

```
F C X F A C O U G H T F Z O L C
D C S A F H I K M D A S F T M H
G Y A X A L O O F J N C O Z X E
F S F F R T B D H U A E L T N F
L J E Y Z O F G F R Q N A P L Z
T Z H F F X U F Y G F O C F B D
Z E X O C A C G O H N U K E L A
Y F G O L D T P H T Y G A I M C
C I F R P Z T Z C X R H F L L D
L N Y L L E A F T R Z F M E F Z
T K F B N D O F A Y E K T B L O
R Y O F F E I H C J C E R A D G
P U F F M L K F S H K N F M F L
```

Crossword Puzzle: /F/ Initial Position

ACROSS

3. forever
4. fable
6. phobia
7. four
8. fever

DOWN

1. feathers
2. feed
3. feud
4. favorite
5. fire
6. phone
7. fiction
8. father

Crossword Puzzle: /F/ Medial Position

ACROSS

1. sofa
4. defend
5. buffalo
7. breakfast
8. thankful
9. spiteful

DOWN

1. suffer
2. selfish
3. thoroughfare
5. before
6. cafeteria
7. barefoot

Crossword Puzzle: /F/ Final Position

ACROSS	DOWN
1. leaf	1. laugh
4. graph	2. safe
5. tough	3. sheriff
8. wife	4. giraffe
9. off	5. thief
10. if	6. huff
	7. roof

/G/ ANSWER KEYS

Word Circles: /G/ Initial Position

girl, gully, goose, gang

Word Circles: /G/ Medial Position

ago, sugar, wagon, anger

Word Circles: /G/ Final Position

flag, frog, twig, sing

Dotted Words: /G/ Initial Position

go, giggle

Dotted Words: /G/ Medial Position

ego, forgot

Dotted Words: /G/ Final Position

egg, fog

Secret Codes: /G/ Initial Position

1. gale	6. golden
2. guess	7. gumdrop
3. gaze	8. gory
4. guilt	9. geyser
5. gust	10. goblet

Secret Codes: /G/ Medial Position

1. alligator	6. agony
2. tiger	7. spaghetti
3. cougar	8. vinegar
4. disgust	9. eggnog
5. hexagon	10. kangaroo

Secret Codes: /G/ Final Position

1. gang	6. polliwog
2. bug	7. hot dog
3. frog	8. washrag
4. fatigue	9. rug
5. catalog	10. zigzag

Scrambled Words: /G/ Initial Position

1. gate	9. gorgeous
2. gaze	10. gab
3. golf	11. girth
4. gulf	12. gather
5. gasoline	13. geyser
6. guilt	14. ghost
7. guard	15. gavel
8. getaway	

Scrambled Words: /G/ Medial Position

1. cougar	9. spaghetti
2. bigger	10. anger
3. finger	11. disgust
4. dragon	12. disguise
5. again	13. wagon
6. tiger	14. negative
7. together	15. regular
8. agony	

Scrambled Words: /G/ Final Position

1. tag	9. catalog
2. bag	10. hug
3. rag	11. league
4. twig	12. vague
5. frog	13. clog
6. hot dog	14. dialogue
7. fatigue	15. nutmeg
8. bug	

Word Find: /G/ Initial Position

245

Word Find: /G/ Medial Position

```
L I A D F Q Z B E K F I L Y M R B
D T U E I L K J I Z M E G O W E G
N T H M C A F D L G F A J G R U S
E E R Y L J I S H T D Q S A G A G
G H G F D S N P N I P A N D P T V
A G Y G G O G N X E G G S H E L L
T A V U G M E T H O V A R V F C K
I P I K G X R U A G S I Z Y Q R M
V S Z Q R N G O G A X N B K A S E
E K X V A T M G A T P S A G W A O
T I C Z G B W X I Y J T U B G C A
G W L G G G G H N D G O K E F T D
B I G G E S T O U G C V R A Y C E
M G A Z B A G G A G E K S G B S G
```

Word Find: /G/ Final Position

```
J U Q H F A T I G U E G P B
R R V S M G Y L O G F D N Z
E I O V F I G N C X K H G E
N J G E M K G H O W A M Y U
E R U N O G U Z N O F G G I
G L E U D C Y G D T V A A R
E Q D T B L T B A G E T T
W K O M F C A T A L O G S T
P H X E S G H C B U G D X N
T L I G A G T F L A G U B I
```

Crossword Puzzle: /G/ Final Position

ACROSS	DOWN
2. fatigue	1. bag
4. catalog	2. fog
7. dog	3. tug
9. washrag	5. leg
10. frog	6. dialogue
12. icebag	7. dig
	8. brag
	11. wig

/J/ ANSWER KEYS

Word Circles: /J/ Initial Position
jolly, just, gym, gyrate

Word Circles: /J/ Medial Position
wager, legit, vigil, eject

Word Circles: /J/ Final Position
gage, sage, stage, wedge

Dotted Words: /J/ Initial Position
jelly, genial

Dotted Words: /J/ Medial Position
edges, villager

Dotted Words: /J/ Final Position
average, image

Crossword Puzzle: /G/ Initial Position

ACROSS	DOWN
1. gardener	1. government
3. good	2. goat
4. gardenia	3. gasoline
5. gamble	4. gorilla
6. gossip	5. goodbye
8. geese	6. gallon
9. going	7. guest
11. give	10. game

Crossword Puzzle: /G/ Medial Position

ACROSS	DOWN
2. saga	1. magazines
5. spaghetti	3. tiger
7. legal	4. magnificent
8. finger	6. alligator
10. eager	7. luggage
11. cigar	9. meager
12. cougar	

Secret Codes: /J/ Initial Position

1. jury	6. giant
2. jet	7. juice
3. gym	8. jacket
4. jaw	9. jelly
5. jerked	10. jolly

Secret Codes: /J/ Medial Position

1. budget	6. adjust
2. nitrogen	7. tragic
3. digest	8. cages
4. wages	9. objected
5. reject	10. agent

Secret Codes: /J/ Final Position

1. dodge	6. dosage
2. message	7. stage
3. voyage	8. porridge
4. language	9. fudge
5. abridge	10. overage

Scrambled Words: /J/ Initial Position

1. justice	9. jewel
2. jolly	10. junior
3. genes	11. Jupiter
4. janitor	12. jungle
5. giant	13. genuine
6. genius	14. geology
7. jelly	15. journal
8. general	

Scrambled Words: /J/ Medial Position

1. oxygen	9. teenager
2. agency	10. refrigerator
3. rejoice	11. ajar
4. wages	12. major
5. tragedy	13. majesty
6. digest	14. religion
7. object	15. biology
8. intelligent	

Scrambled Words: /J/ Final Position

1. cage	9. package
2. page	10. storage
3. garbage	11. salvage
4. damage	12. voyage
5. marriage	13. village
6. luggage	14. beverage
7. strange	15. advantage
8. average	

Word Find: /J/ Initial Position

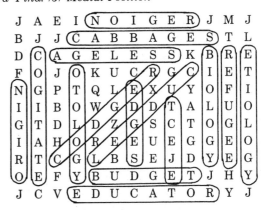

Word Find: /J/ Medial Position

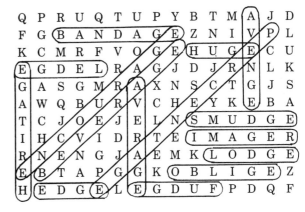

Word Find: /J/ Final Position

Crossword Puzzle: /J/ Initial Position

ACROSS	DOWN
1. juice	1. jolt
2. joyful	2. junior
3. juvenile	3. junction
4. jar	5. jumbo
6. genuine	6. gym
7. journey	7. jewel
8. joke	
9. jelly	

Crossword Puzzle: /J/ Medial Position

ACROSS	DOWN
1. oxygen	1. object
2. eject	3. tragic
5. gadget	4. wages
6. soldier	7. legend
9. frigid	8. rigid

Crossword Puzzle: /J/ Final Position

ACROSS	DOWN
2. village	1. page
4. garbage	2. voyage
7. edge	3. luggage
8. damage	5. bridge
10. cage	6. rage
	9. message

Secret Codes: /K/ Final Position

1. earache	6. yolk
2. terrific	7. thick
3. frantic	8. critic
4. stick	9. static
5. athletic	10. alike

Scrambled Words: /K/ Initial Position

1. courteous	9. coin
2. curious	10. cough
3. kindergarten	11. kind
4. caught	12. kindle
5. kite	13. kiss
6. keyhole	14. conversation
7. coffee	15. cabinet
8. kitten	

/K/ ANSWER KEYS

Word Circles: /K/ Initial Position

carry, kiss, count, curl

Word Circles: /K/ Medial Position

market, across, okay, buckle

Word Circles: /K/ Final Position

black, music, sick, check

Dotted Words: /K/ Initial Position

cozy, call

Dotted Words: /K/ Medial Position

parked, trinkets

Dotted Words: /K/ Final Position

stock, lock

Secret Codes: /K/ Initial Position

1. cook	6. condition
2. cabin	7. caffeine
3. kettle	8. keyhole
4. call	9. colorful
5. cattle	10. cabinet

Secret Codes: /K/ Medial Position

1. napkin	6. macaroni
2. baker	7. seacoast
3. recover	8. echo
4. cracker	9. acne
5. bobcat	10. locket

Scrambled Words: /K/ Medial Position

1. baking	9. acne
2. jacket	10. chicken
3. background	11. vacation
4. sneakers	12. factory
5. because	13. location
6. looking	14. macaroni
7. cooking	15. helicopter
8. bacon	

Scrambled Words: /K/ Final Position

1. arithmetic	9. chick
2. toothpick	10. terrific
3. snake	11. look
4. cupcake	12. walk
5. sick	13. steak
6. awake	14. break
7. duck	15. o'clock
8. stomach	

Word Find: /K/ Initial Position

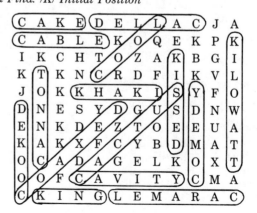

Word Find: /K/ Medial Position

```
F  R  U  E  B  Z  X  Q  S  K  Y  T  R  R  X  H  U  S
L  T  J  L  O  T  N  E  D  I  C  C  A  T  D  Q  A  R
P  K  W  T  C  L  S  J  U  T  Z  L  T  M  Y  M  E  W
U  M  I  T  Z  H  U  R  R  I  C  A  N  E  N  V  Z  Q
W  H  U  E  A  P  V  O  V  N  Z  S  B  X  O  O  P  F
K  C  Q  K  M  P  O  C  K  E  T  C  M  C  U  C  V  B
G  T  I  A  B  I  C  K  E  R  A  Q  E  W  Y  A  L  E
S  N  Y  E  N  C  R  A  C  K  E  R  S  A  L  L  Y  K
G  V  B  T  Z  B  E  C  A  M  E  X  G  C  O  I  A  D
S  F  R  A  V  S  N  E  A  K  E  R  S  N  C  Z  O  J
O  B  Y  E  R  W  R  E  K  A  B  W  L  E  O  E  P  D
V  T  N  W  D  S  U  C  C  E  E  D  X  Q  N  Z  I  A
```

Word Find: /K/ Final Position

```
A  A  W  L  A  R  T  I  S  T  I  C  Z  D
C  Y  S  O  C  K  Z  D  X  G  I  Y  E  F
A  N  T  I  Q  U  E  F  P  T  Q  F  X  Q
B  V  W  O  K  E  O  K  E  P  O  C  H  Z
Z  M  X  P  M  S  B  M  S  R  D  L  I  E
C  H  E  C  K  X  H  C  H  S  T  E  A  K
U  R  N  L  J  T  K  F  U  T  P  H  O  A
T  Y  T  G  I  G  A  N  T  I  C  V  K  T
Q  O  B  R  O  D  N  E  Q  C  G  I  L  R
P  L  A  Q  U  E  P  U  M  K  J  W  R  E
C  K  T  D  Z  B  W  R  E  C  K  J  N  V
A  Y  S  P  A  T  R  I  O  T  I  C  V  O
```

Crossword Puzzle: /K/ Initial Position

ACROSS	DOWN
1. collar	1. conduct
2. coin	2. colorful
4. careful	3. cute
5. combat	4. communicate
6. kidnapped	6. kick
7. cola	
8. keep	

Crossword Puzzle: /K/ Medial Position

ACROSS	DOWN
1. pocket	1. pumpkin
2. breakfast	2. broken
5. acorn	3. second
6. napkin	4. bacon
8. soccer	7. pecan

Crossword Puzzle: /K/ Final Position

ACROSS	DOWN
1. attic	2. chalk
4. racetrack	3. yardstick
5. storybook	6. oak
7. brick	7. back
8. knock	9. cake

/L/ ANSWER KEYS

Word Circles: /L/ Initial Position

lawn, lodge, lava, loaf

Word Circles: /L/ Medial Position

alley, ruler, halt, elect

Word Circles: /L/ Final Position

medal, gravel, pupil, pearl

Dotted Words: /L/ Initial Position

laughed, like

Dotted Words: /L/ Medial Position

silver, children

Dotted Words: /L/ Final Position

all, smile

Secret Codes: /L/ Initial Position

1. litter	6. lit
2. loaf	7. lamp
3. lousy	8. loan
4. laughing	9. like
5. lucky	10. lumpy

Secret Codes: /L/ Medial Position

1. violent	6. alarm
2. reality	7. ability
3. allergy	8. cellar
4. bowling	9. billion
5. gaily	10. usually

Secret Codes: /L/ Final Position

1. spoil	6. musical
2. feel	7. fuel
3. equal	8. style
4. awhile	9. owl
5. gradual	10. casual

Scrambled Words: /L/ Initial Position

1. lunch
2. letter
3. library
4. laundry
5. lazy
6. ladder
7. lawn mower
8. legs
9. lotion
10. look
11. lesson
12. lump
13. lucky
14. lost
15. law

Scrambled Words: /L/ Medial Position

1. cola
2. monopoly
3. color
4. balance
5. dollar
6. gorilla
7. alone
8. telephone
9. electric
10. balloon
11. chilly
12. alarm
13. smelling
14. envelope
15. family

Scrambled Words: /L/ Final Position

1. refill
2. pencil
3. basketball
4. casserole
5. vowel
6. muscle
7. towel
8. sea gull
9. control
10. awhile
11. ball
12. hole
13. oil
14. call
15. tail

Word Find: /L/ Initial Position

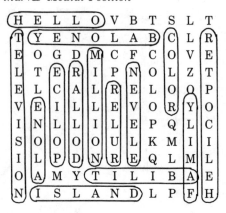

Word Find: /L/ Medial Position

Word Find: /L/ Final Position

Crossword Puzzle: /L/ Initial Position

ACROSS
1. lake
3. lumberjack
5. lifesaver
8. letter
9. lavender
11. loiter
12. loot

DOWN
1. lemonade
2. later
3. librarian
4. leader
5. like
6. litter
7. liar
10. lotion

Crossword Puzzle: /L/ Medial Position

ACROSS
1. jelly
3. elevate
4. helicopter
9. police
10. ruler
11. color
12. happily
13. polite

DOWN
2. eleven
5. intelligent
6. television
7. hello
8. pillow
12. holly

Crossword Puzzle: /L/ Final Position

ACROSS
1. oatmeal
4. meatballs
6. fuel
7. tadpole
9. rascal
11. all
13. ball
14. swimming pool

DOWN
2. meal
3. baseball
4. muscle
5. tall
6. football
8. doll
10. control
12. cancel

/R/ ANSWER KEYS

Word Circles: /R/ Initial Position
rocket, right, ready, round

Word Circles: /R/ Medial Position
camera, diary, carrot, hornet

Word Circles: /R/ Final Position
tower, paper, doctor, store

Dotted Words: /R/ Initial Position

romance, remedy

Dotted Words: /R/ Medial Position

marrow, oriole

Dotted Words: /R/ Final Position

eclair, velour

Secret Codes: /R/ Initial Position

1. reject
2. roof
3. ready
4. rage
5. rest
6. wrist
7. rainy
8. writer
9. really
10. regular

Secret Codes: /R/ Medial Position

1. parade
2. orange
3. weary
4. syrup
5. terror
6. sorrow
7. very
8. area
9. horrible
10. serious

Secret Codes: /R/ Final Position

1. fire
2. before
3. ignore
4. outdoor
5. where
6. guitar
7. umpire
8. compare
9. tour
10. sour

Scrambled Words: /R/ Initial Position

1. write
2. railroad
3. wriggle
4. ring
5. relax
6. raisin
7. wrap
8. wrong
9. round
10. rabbit
11. radio
12. roses
13. wrestling
14. respect
15. riddle

Scrambled Words: /R/ Medial Position

1. salary
2. dictionary
3. terrible
4. vocabulary
5. tomorrow
6. berry
7. theory
8. secretary
9. ceremony
10. auditorium
11. parent
12. starry
13. area
14. calories
15. everyday

Scrambled Words: /R/ Final Position

1. dinosaur
2. rooster
3. disappear
4. rocker
5. anywhere
6. writer
7. ruler
8. ear
9. star
10. somewhere
11. hear
12. sir
13. your
14. ignore
15. fear

Word Find: /R/ Initial Position

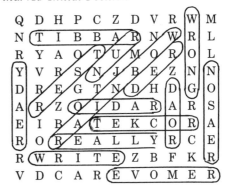

Word Find: /R/ Medial Position

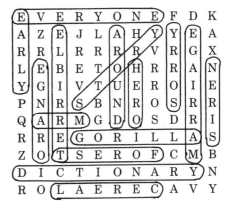

Word Find: /R/ Final Position

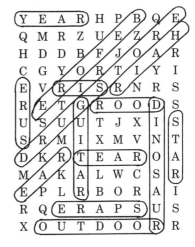

Crossword Puzzle: /R/ Initial Position

ACROSS	DOWN
1. regard	1. recreation
3. rug	2. regret
4. refrigerate	5. regular
7. run	6. remark
8. rural	8. rear
10. relax	9. reply

251

Crossword Puzzle: /R/ Medial Position

ACROSS	DOWN
3. marriage	1. zero
5. arrow	2. period
6. hurry	3. marine
7. narrow	4. garage
10. arid	8. word
11. terrible	9. around
12. boring	12. berry
13. dirty	

Crossword Puzzle: /R/ Final Position

ACROSS	DOWN
1. dinosaur	1. door
3. pear	2. supper
4. are	5. smear
6. nightmare	6. near
9. adore	7. guitar
11. four	8. before
12. pair	10. explore

/S/ ANSWER KEYS

Word Circles: /S/ Initial Position

silly, cereal, seed, city

Word Circles: /S/ Medial Position

castle, person, acid, fossil

Word Circles: /S/ Final Position

dress, grass, less, dance

Dotted Words: /S/ Initial Position

sandbar, seaweed

Dotted Words: /S/ Medial Position

voices, aerosol

Dotted Words: /S/ Final Position

campus, alias

Secret Codes: /S/ Initial Position

1. sea	6. city
2. sad	7. phychic
3. sign	8. salesman
4. second	9. seashell
5. celery	10. sympathy

Secret Codes: /S/ Medial Position

1. aerosol	6. basic
2. voices	7. crossing
3. dressing	8. bison
4. bracelet	9. basin
5. courtesy	10. icy

Secret Codes: /S/ Final Position

1. octopus	6. witness
2. mess	7. bookcase
3. fireplace	8. class
4. bass	9. lettuce
5. juice	10. chorus

Scrambled Words: /S/ Initial Position

1. saddle	9. seashell
2. circle	10. ceiling
3. super	11. sunburn
4. citizen	12. cereal
5. solo	13. siren
6. solution	14. syrup
7. sidewalk	15. soprano
8. sunny	

Scrambled Words: /S/ Medial Position

1. bracelet	9. rhinoceros
2. glasses	10. beside
3. innocent	11. recipe
4. officer	12. decimal
5. necessary	13. icicle
6. eraser	14. medicine
7. casserole	15. electricity
8. babysit	

Scrambled Words: /S/ Final Position

1. face	9. office
2. class	10. price
3. bus	11. necklace
4. race	12. police
5. sis	13. walrus
6. chorus	14. practice
7. delicious	15. adios
8. sense	

Word Find: /S/ Initial Position

Word Find: /S/ Medial Position

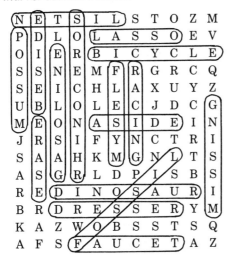

Word Find: /S/ Final Position

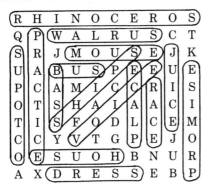

Crossword Puzzle: /S/ Initial Position

ACROSS	DOWN
1. signs	1. seven
3. sack	2. supermarket
5. sanity	3. Santa Claus
6. seance	4. city
8. cent	7. sit
9. saltern	9. south
10. sap	
11. seem	
12. sanctum	

Crossword Puzzle: /S/ Medial Position

ACROSS	DOWN
1. castle	1. chaser
3. fossil	2. lasso
5. missing	3. fantasy
6. peso	4. lessen
7. gossip	6. parasol
9. icy	8. positive
10. bracelet	10. babysit
11. officer	12. closer
13. muscle	
14. receipt	

Crossword Puzzle: /S/ Final Position

ACROSS	DOWN
1. gorgeous	1. greenhouse
4. tennis	2. race
6. reduce	3. octopus
8. us	5. nutritious
9. twice	7. chess
10. vase	10. voice
11. juice	12. cross
13. careless	14. lass
15. yes	
16. chorus	

/SH/ ANSWER KEYS

Word Circles: /SH/ Initial Position

shop, shawl, shelf, shade

Word Circles: /SH/ Medial Position

ashes, ocean, usher, tissue

Word Circles: /SH/ Final Position

brush, marsh, trash, cash

Dotted Words: /SH/ Initial Position

shaggy, share

Dotted Words: /SH/ Medial Position

pushed, election

Dotted Words: /SH/ Final Position

fish, fresh

Secret Codes: /SH/ Initial Position

1. shame	6. shadow
2. shovel	7. should
3. show	8. shark
4. chic	9. sure
5. shower	10. shook

Secret Codes: /SH/ Medial Position

1. cashier	6. worship
2. dishes	7. luxury
3. special	8. imitation
4. cushion	9. location
5. lotion	10. suspicion

Secret Codes: /SH/ Final Position

1. crush	6. eyelash
2. squash	7. push
3. finish	8. harsh
4. flash	9. licorice
5. wish	10. foolish

Scrambled Words: /SH/ Initial Position

1. shake	9. chef
2. sharp	10. short
3. sugar	11. chalet
4. shuttle	12. shiver
5. shy	13. shovel
6. shirt	14. shabby
7. she	15. shelter
8. show	

Scrambled Words: /SH/ Medial Position

1. pushing	9. technician
2. caution	10. musician
3. washer	11. education
4. tissue	12. dictionary
5. vacation	13. fisherman
6. action	14. ashes
7. addition	15. social
8. bushes	

Scrambled Words: /SH/ Final Position

1. selfish	9. wish
2. brush	10. punish
3. splash	11. unselfish
4. fish	12. toothbrush
5. cash	13. crush
6. trash	14. licorice
7. wash	15. radish
8. refresh	

Word Find: /SH/ Initial Position

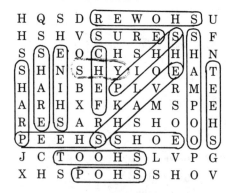

Word Find: /SH/ Medial Position

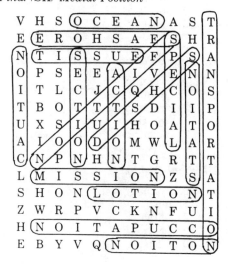

Word Find: /SH/ Final Position

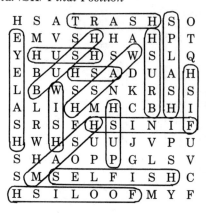

Crossword Puzzle: /SH/ Initial Position

ACROSS	DOWN
1. shoelaces	1. shampoo
5. ship	2. chauffeur
6. chef	3. short
7. shout	4. shift
8. sherbet	5. shoot
9. show	7. sheets
10. shine	8. shower
	9. shield
	10. she

Crossword Puzzle: /SH/ Medial Position

ACROSS	DOWN
2. option	1. seashore
3. wishbone	2. ocean
5. nation	3. worship
6. fashion	4. bashful
9. caution	7. section
10. occupation	8. tension

Crossword Puzzle: /SH/ Final Position

ACROSS	DOWN
3. ambush	1. rush
4. goldfish	2. hairbrush
6. rash	4. garnish
8. paintbrush	5. radish
11. unselfish	7. squash
13. push	9. accomplish
14. hush	10. splash
	12. gash

/T/ ANSWER KEYS

Word Circles: /T/ Initial Position

tuna, teeth, toast, today

Word Circles: /T/ Medial Position

attic, pinto, sixty, motor

Word Circles: /T/ Final Position

sunset, skate, state, wheat

Dotted Words: /T/ Initial Position

tonsil, topaz

Dotted Words: /T/ Medial Position

motor, hotel

Dotted Words: /T/ Final Position

yacht, knot

Secret Codes: /T/ Initial Position

1. tender
2. ten
3. tell
4. tongue
5. today
6. together
7. tulips
8. towel
9. turtle
10. TV

Secret Codes: /T/ Medial Position

1. attic
2. hotel
3. eating
4. better
5. duties
6. computer
7. potato
8. vitamins
9. kitten
10. quitter

Secret Codes: /T/ Final Position

1. jet
2. gate
3. fruit
4. about
5. state
6. operate
7. knot
8. skate
9. wallet
10. unfit

Scrambled Words: /T/ Initial Position

1. tools
2. taste
3. total
4. television
5. tomato
6. talk
7. teenager
8. table
9. teeth
10. take
11. taxicab
12. turtle
13. tired
14. toolbox
15. taco

Scrambled Words: /T/ Medial Position

1. city
2. heater
3. button
4. cotton
5. beauty
6. located
7. writer
8. elevator
9. water
10. visitor
11. forgotten
12. potato
13. theater
14. operator
15. hospital

Scrambled Words: /T/ Final Position

1. wet
2. coat
3. pocket
4. boat
5. upset
6. jacket
7. cat
8. get
9. ate
10. forgot
11. plate
12. clarinet
13. violet
14. supermarket
15. coconut

Word Find: /T/ Initial Position

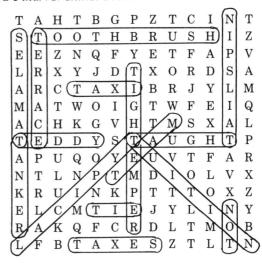

Word Find: /T/ Medial Position

Word Find: /T/ Final Position

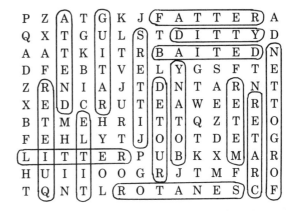

Crossword Puzzle: /T/ Initial Position

ACROSS	DOWN
3. try	1. teenager
4. television	2. timid
5. tickle	3. tired
6. teakettle	4. teacher
9. tantrum	5. time
10. temper	7. together
	8. turn
	9. trim

Crossword Puzzle: /T/ Medial Position

ACROSS	DOWN
3. pretty	1. rattle
5. data	2. batter
6. potato	3. photograph
7. tutor	4. total
8. lettuce	9. tomato
11. mittens	10. city
14. guitar	12. naughty
15. water	13. motor

Crossword Puzzle: /T/ Final Position

ACROSS	DOWN
1. chocolate	1. compliment
5. thought	2. operate
7. coat	3. light
8. ate	4. meet
10. suit	6. goat
12. shut	7. create
	9. eat
	10. seat
	11. it
	12. spot

/V/ ANSWER KEYS

Word Circles: /V/ Initial Position

vine, vowel, visit, voice

Word Circles: /V/ Medial Position

oval, cover, navel, silver

Word Circles: /V/ Final Position

wave, glove, sleeve, cave

Dotted Words: /V/ Initial Position

vagrant, viper

Dotted Words: /V/ Medial Position

cavity, haven

Dotted Words: /V/ Final Position

sleeve, glove

Secret Codes: /V/ Initial Position

1. veto	6. village
2. valley	7. virus
3. valid	8. verify
4. vines	9. visit
5. visible	10. verbal

Secret Codes: /V/ Medial Position

1. adverb	6. having
2. gravy	7. flavor
3. cover	8. overalls
4. ever	9. poverty
5. event	10. seventy

Secret Codes: /V/ Final Position

1. leave	6. cave
2. we've	7. five
3. prove	8. forgive
4. sleeve	9. olive
5. retrieve	10. arrive

Scrambled Words: /V/ Initial Position

1. veto	9. vowel
2. villain	10. voice
3. victory	11. village
4. volcano	12. voile
5. vacation	13. velvet
6. violet	14. vents
7. verb	15. vision
8. van	

Scrambled Words: /V/ Medial Position

1. clever	9. develop
2. overtime	10. fever
3. everybody	11. eleven
4. beaver	12. seven
5. even	13. heaven
6. forever	14. oven
7. devote	15. deliver
8. driver	

Scrambled Words: /V/ Final Position

1. relieve	9. remove
2. gave	10. have
3. improve	11. shave
4. above	12. stove
5. believe	13. love
6. drive	14. expensive
7. relative	15. arrive
8. brave	

Word Find: /V/ Initial Position

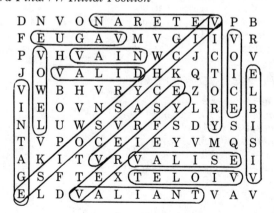

Word Find: /V/ Medial Position

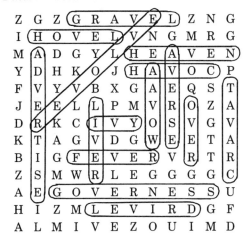

Word Find: /V/ Final Position

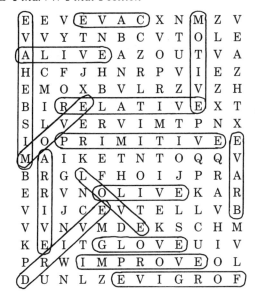

Crossword Puzzle: /V/ Initial Position

ACROSS	DOWN
2. vacant	1. van
3. violin	2. valley
6. verbal	3. vapor
7. vertigo	4. vanilla
8. vicarage	5. vowel
9. viper	7. version

Crossword Puzzle: /V/ Medial Position

ACROSS	DOWN
2. covering	1. deliver
3. seventh	4. navy
5. bravery	5. beaver
7. lava	6. review
8. over	
9. elevator	

Crossword Puzzle: /V/ Final Position

ACROSS	DOWN
3. primitive	1. dive
6. thrive	2. give
8. love	3. positive
10. above	4. expensive
	5. five
	7. olive
	9. gave